THE STRANGERS ON MY ROOF

THIS is basically the story of the vicissitudes and ultimate break-up of a lack-lustre marriage, of Chloe, a speech-therapist – and her professional skills are cunningly inter-woven into the story – who unwillingly accompanies her conventional husband to his new job in Hong Kong, to find that their different responses to this often startling new environment only deepen their estrangement. It is as a furtive secret that Chloe succours the refugee family from China who live, as so many refugees must, on the roofs of other people's houses; but the bread she casts on their waters is at last and surprisingly returned to her in the form of lasting happiness.

E. ARNOT ROBERTSON

THE STRANGERS ON MY ROOF

LONDON : THE CRESSET PRESS

First published in Great Britain in 1964 by
The Cresset Press, 11 Fitzroy Square, London, W.1.
Printed in Great Britain at the St. Ann's Press, Park Road, Altrincham

CONTENTS

CHAPTER I

Liar-dice

'YOUR NAME'S CHLOE, isn't it?' said the stranger beside me in the railway carriage.

'Yes.' I answered without surprise, and without interest in how he knew. I was dazed still by the impact of something my husband had told me just before I left our house to go to the Clinic where I worked: news which threatened everything that mattered to me. 'I'm Chloe.'

'So I'm on to who you are, but I bet you can't place me!'

'Let me see, can I?' I dragged my attention into the railway carriage and looked at him: rather small, rather dark, young-middle-aged: one of the mass of undistinguished people, like myself, pouring into London from the suburbs in the rush hour, on their way to the day's job.

'No, you can't, so don't pretend you remember where we met.'

'All right. I don't.' A pathetically aggressive little man, he seemed glad to have someone – anyone – at a disadvantage. I had no desire to talk. As much as I wanted anything in this half-stunned state, I wanted to go on staring out of the window, listening to the train wheels. 'Hong Kong? Hong Kong?' they sang, and as we ran over points, 'You go to Hong Kong? You go to Hong Kong?' I wanted to think, as best I could, before being caught up in the routine and rush of appointments at the Clinic: it was going to be a difficult day.

Had I shown anything of what I felt when my husband

announced – almost casually, but watching me closely, I believed – 'I might hear today if I'm getting charge of our Far East Branch. If so, it would mean living in Hong Kong?' No, I was almost sure that I had given nothing away.

Supposing that he got his promotion, could I bear to leave England, losing all that I had built, here, of a life of my own: my love as well as my work? Or did I desperately want to go, anywhere: to escape, to make a clean break with what I knew, in one part of my mind, could not last much longer? Either way, it seemed singularly unimportant that someone whom I failed to recognize was aware of my name. Then from far off, as it were, I was sorry to have disappointed him by such blighting indifference – 'Do, please, tell me how you knew me?'

'Funny little scar on your chin. Like a J. Remember thinking, when I first saw you, "Now if it wasn't for that scar she'd be quite a pretty girl." Why didn't you have it removed? They can do that sort of thing, easy enough, these days.'

'Because I never thought it mattered much. As you say, it's small.' What was eating into him, I wondered, to make him quite so truculent? He could hardly be like this all the time, with everyone.

'Queer my noticing it, really, when you were the first girl I saw after coming out of prison camp! You'd think all I'd say to myself was, "There's a girl!" Even if you were in uniform. You gave me some advice I'm damn glad I didn't take. Oh, very pressing with it you were. And you know what I was thinking all the time you were talking? "Pity about that scar." My wife's initial, J. My wife that was, then. J. for Joan. Probably why I noticed it specially.'

'Where was it we talked?'

If only I could be certain that I had shown nothing more than natural interest and concern, at the idea of being suddenly uprooted. No, no, no – resentment swept over me – let me not have to give up so much, so suddenly! Not with such

2

heartbreak as going away now was bound to mean to me. And to someone else, what would it mean?

'Airfield in Belgium. Towards the end of the War. Melbroek near Brussels – that bring back anything? You were in the W.A.A.F.'

'So you were one of the P.O.W.s who collected there for the last hop home.' Even through my preoccupation the scene came back vividly; the bleak airfield, on the windy spring day, twelve years before; the dirty, eager faces of men streaming past me, to domestic disaster in many cases. There had been so few I had been able to waylay successfully: I had evidently failed with him. This was one of the strangest, and, for me, personally, dramatic moments of the war – which seemed such a long time ago in my life, but not, I felt, in the life of the man beside me in the train.

In that last spring of the war, with the German front line crumbling, the prison camps were being over-run by advancing Allied troops. The gates stood open, and men who had been three, four or five years away from their wives wandered out on to the roads and jumped an army lorry or hitch-hiked to the nearest airfield. There, the young bomber pilots, more knowledgeable about death than life, turned gaily to the job of getting them home without delay. I could still see the great Lancasters swooping down out of the sky: the crews, as they landed, leaving the engines running and leaning out shouting, 'Pile in, boys. England in forty minutes.' Often a man was not more than four hours from the time he left prison camp to the time he reached his own front door. And on the airfield there were two other W.A.A.F. officers, besides myself, who realised that England in 1945 was not a place to which prisoners of war of long standing could safely return with no warning of their coming.

Relieved of official duties for the time being, we were handing out cups of tea, and welcoming smiles, and food if anyone would wait to eat it. Unofficially, we buttonholed man after man – how it all came back! The urgency and the anxiety and the vicarious distress – and tried to get him to take advantage of the free telegraphic service provided for returning prisoners. 'Give me your name and address, and I'll see your family knows you're coming.' Give your wife or your girl, time, if necessary, to take the dollars out of her handbag, the unsuitable snapshots off the mantelpiece. No man had the right to expect that through years of war, time would stand still for the free, as it had for the prisoners. But this they expected.

'Not on your life, sweetheart! See this?' The tougher the prison camp, the closer a man had clung to his dream. 'This' was sometimes a photograph, more often his civilian latchkey, kept as a talisman. Through dreary days and nights he had imagined himself walking up a well-known path, to open a well-known door. 'She' would be cooking, and look up with surprise turning to incredulous joy, and the children would rush out, shouting 'Daddy!' The return would be all wonder and delight.

For the three of us, stationed by chance at Melbroek at that moment, it was impossible to believe that this was how it would be, in most cases. Each of us, out of kindness, evolved a piece of appropriate patter to run off to any man who disclosed, in the garrulous pleasure of talking to a woman again, over those cups of tea, that he was either married or had someone special waiting for him, or at any rate supposed he had. All our patter was probably much the same: I could still remember my opening: 'Look, you've had your great moment – liberation. But she hasn't had hers yet. That'll be when you get back. You can't be selfish about this. I'm telling you, as a girl, she'll never forgive you if you don't let her have the chance to get her hair done, and wear the dress she's been saving up for just this. Oh, of course I know what she's wearing doesn't matter to you. But I know, as another woman, how much it matters to her, see? So if you'll just

4

write down your name and home address, I'll – ' If I ran off my little speech too quickly it failed to convince, as it must have done with this man who remembered I was Chloe. Nearly every man said, 'What's your name?' and used it as if it were something sweet in his mouth. If I went slowly I was aware of all those hurrying past me to meet – what?

People, when not actually faithless or unkind, were as often as not unimaginative. 'Oh, how like you, Jim, turning up today. Now I've got my sister coming over for the afternoon. Well, I know you don't care for her, but what am I supposed to do, she's in the bus by this time. You'll just have to put up with it, or go round to your brother's or something, till she's gone. There isn't a bus back for her till seven, you can't expect her to wait in the street,' and the homecoming would be flat and spoiled. A shrunken Scottish major, in a much decorated tunic too big for him, refused his address and confided to me his fear that his sons had been ruling the roost in his absence. 'Sent themselves to school in England! Glasgow not good enough. I can't get back too fast to stop that sort of nonsense. They're going to know who's home.' Poor devil, I thought helplessly, with young hatred coming to him so soon, and he actually impatient for it. It was odd that I remembered the Scottish major so clearly from that day, but not my fellow-passenger at all.

'You wanted to know where I lived, and told me a lot of blather about my wife tarting herself up for me. That's a laugh – ! A lot of tarting she'd have done for me. I said, "What're you called?" and you said, "Chloe." So I told you, "Well, Chloe, nothing doing! I'm going to be the big gasp, round where I belong." I was the big gasp, all right, walking in on them. I picked up my son – three years old, he was. I'd never seen him, though I'd known he was on the way when I went overseas. Just as well I did know that. If I hadn't, maybe I wouldn't have believed he was mine, the way things were.

5

I've never seen her since. And you wanted to help pull wool over my eyes! Am I pleased I didn't listen!'

There was no sense in pointing out, 'Perhaps you'd have been happier if you had.' I said nothing. He turned jauntier. 'Oh, well. Lot of water gone under a lot of bridges since then. Doesn't matter now. You married?'

'Yes.'

'But you go to work. I wouldn't let my wife do that. If I'd married again, I mean. Not me, though. Once bitten, twice shy! Lot of funny people around, these days.'

'Some women prefer to work. You might find it difficult to stop her, if your wife happened to like the job she was doing. And I like mine. Very much.' Indeed, how much! The possibility of being forced to give it up lay like a grey shadow over the bright spring morning.

'What is it?'

'I'm a speech-therapist. I work three days a week at a Clinic in Hammersmith, one day in north London, and one day and most evenings at home, on private work. So I'd better like what I do, hadn't I?'

'I suppose so.' He sounded uninterested. 'Myself, I'm on Post Office Maintenance. Telephones, you know. Not a bad job. Pay isn't too hot, but you never know what you'll get next. In the way of repairs. Go all over the place.' Suddenly something struck him. 'Speech – you cure stammers?'

'I treat them. Stammering is about the trickiest thing people in my line ever have to tackle.'

'My boy stammers.'

Again I refrained from saying something: that I was hardly surprised. 'I'm sorry about that. It's a wretched handicap. I expect he's still at school, and other children are so merciless.'

'Think you could cure him?'

'No. Probably not. How can I say without knowing him? There are lots of different kinds of stammer. I could possibly

6

help him to manage his better, and perhaps mind less about it. And not go back to the beginning of the sentence whenever he meets a block.'

'Yes!' the man said as if amazed. 'He does do that!'

What he had not said was so plain. 'Fancy you knowing something about your job.' Even something as simple and fundamental as that.

'You know, Chloe, I wouldn't mind his coming to your Clinic. The Hammersmith one. Not too far from us. That's a compliment I'm paying you!'

'Thank you, but I don't think it's a very good idea, all the same,' I said. 'Get him treatment, by all means. He ought to be having that. But not from me. You'd be more confident about him in the hands of a man. And that would be better for him – your feeling that he was getting the best of something. If you like, I can give you the names of several good speech-therapists working within reach of Hammersmith. There's a very able man at the Battersea Hospital. Particularly successful with young people – '

'You high up in your line?'

'This isn't a line you get high up in! It's a very personal job. Either you're interested in voices, and how people use them, and what can go wrong with the apparatus. Or you aren't. I am, which is lucky. Because if you aren't particularly interested – if you're only conscientious, going by the book – your patients don't tend to make much progress. But you don't automatically become famous, you know, by enjoying what you do. Anyway, I've only been qualified about a year and a half.'

My heart contracted again with fear. Hong Kong: more than nine-tenths of the community Chinese-speaking, in spite of its being a British Colony: I knew that already. What could I do there? The whole of my technical training had been for use in my own language. I had found not only satisfaction but, inevitably, the fulfilment of a great part of my own needs, in this particular form of contact with people, this specialised way of helping.

'All your son has to take along to Battersea,' I said, trying to hold my thoughts steady, 'is a note from his headmaster or his school doctor. That's if he's still at school. Or from his employers and your own local doctor, if he's already working.' I made a supreme effort to remember the Battersea speech-therapist's timetable: I had done a fortnight's locum for him at the end of my training. 'Monday and Wednesday afternoon, two to five. Friday, two-thirty to six, I think. But you'd better check that by phone.'

We sat in silence for a minute, while the train wheels sang. He pulled from his wallet and showed me a snapshot discoloured by age, cracked where the curled up corners had been flattened out. 'Came on this the other day, among a lot of papers I hadn't looked at for years. Takes you back, doesn't it? Us playing liar-dice!'

' "Us"?' I said stupidly. Here were four young soldiers, laughing, two of them holding up beer mugs. One of them I could just recognize as the lad he must have been. All the intense nostalgia of time out of reach clung to that faded cheeriness.

'Oh, not you and me! Those are three of the boys who were in the bag with me. Of course this was taken before we left England. You must remember playing liar-dice in the Services? Don't know how the War would have gone on without it! In or out of the bag. Chaps got so keen in our camp, I've known them miss a food-issue. And meals were just about all we had to break up the day.'

'Why, yes! Now you mention it, I do remember that game. And how some people took to it like drink.'

Carefully he put the snapshot, his immortality, back into his wallet. What must his present life be like, I wondered, that the War remained the one reality?

The boredom of hours spent playing liar-dice, on airfields,

8

and in transit messes! Certainly, this came back to me. I had never, at any time, been able to understand the attraction of imitation poker without cards, nor the fanatical eagerness of addicts to know, when a fresh face appeared in any anteroom, whether the owner played or not. If yes, he or she could settle down at once to a quorum, and make friends: if not, getting acquainted tended to be a slower matter. I had therefore learnt to play, as a useful introduction at new postings, but I welcomed every interruption.

Like most addictions, playing liar-dice was at first, to those who succumbed to it, a substitute for more interesting pursuits which had been snatched away by circumstances, by the war. It got them through unwanted time; and then gradually it became more important to them than the loss for which it compensated. There swept over me, in a few seconds of heightened awareness, a feeling of uncertainty which was almost foreboding. A conjecture sprang from the refrain of the train wheels. Was it possible that for me, in the unseeable and at present unplan-able future, something which I took to desperately, as a substitute for living, might become the most essential part of my existence?

We were nearing Victoria Station. 'Tell you something funny about my job,' he said, 'like you did about yours – '

I could see nothing amusing in what I had told him, nor what was funny in his information. It seemed touching.

' – Half the time we're called up by subscribers, wanting us to test their lines because they're sure the phone's out of order, why, there's nothing wrong with them at all. Girls, all of them, those callers. Women, anyway. Been waiting and waiting by the phone because some man said he'd ring up, and then he didn't. They won't believe it's his fault. Oh, no, must be the bell or something. Sure he's been trying, but he can't get through. Will we see the line's clear? "Replace the receiver, madam, and we'll ring you back . . . That all right?" – "Yes, thank you".' He gave a forlorn, squeaky imitation. 'Lot of funny people around these days.' This phrase, I found later, was very frequently on his lips: I never knew at what point in history, from his view, the world had been less full of funny people. 'Look, I think I'd like my boy to come to your Clinic. It's free, isn't it?'

'Yes. National Health. All right, if you're sure you want him to.' The train was slowing down. Hurriedly I gave him the address, the hours of attendance, and had not the heart to tell him that there would be little point in my taking on a new patient if quite soon I should have to relinquish my post there. In any case, I had already more patients than I could conveniently handle, in my three days a week.

The workers streamed out of the train, swirling along the platform, engulfing us, separating us. 'Goodbye,' I called, round a fat Indian encumbered by many sample-cases, who was bawling in a sad falsetto for a porter. They were nonexistent at that hour.

My sour little travelling companion dodged back to me. 'Goodbye, I'm Paul,' he said, as if it were very important that I should remember this. 'Paul. Don't forget.' I was someone from his War.

'No. Goodbye, Paul.'

'Fancy you being Chloe!'

'Extraordinary, isn't it?'

We parted.

Fancy. Chloe! A warm, Mediterranean, over-romantic name. Privately I never thought of myself as Chloe, though I had been called that almost all my life. Whenever I urged myself to face something of which I was afraid, as I was afraid that day, I said inwardly, 'Now, Clo –!', certainly not, 'Now, Chloe – !' Only one person had ever made the name sing for me, by halving it. And this was absurd, I knew, for surely 'Clo' had a poor, workaday sound compared with 'Chloe': except to me.

CHAPTER II

'You Get No Thanks'

SEVERAL TRYING SESSIONS at the Clinic were in their way a blessing, shutting out personal anxieties for a while.

With my first patient I had the awkward job, which I had put off for several weeks out of cowardice, of telling her, as gently as possible, that she must not go on wasting my time as well as her own, by coming to the Clinic if she really did not want to improve. She, too, had a stammer. It was her excuse for not being a more successful musician. She played the violin, rather badly I surmised, in a small Palm Court orchestra. From everything she had told me emerged a picture of all concerned, including the hotel management, going far out of their way to be kind. She might have been sacked long ago, on her performance, without the stammer. Because of it, she claimed, others were unwilling to play with her, no-one would give her a chance.

A woman two or three years my senior – I was thirty-two – she cried for a while like a child deprived of some cherished fantasy, and I felt brutal. It was never my belief that people were necessarily better off without their pitiful pretences, but in her case I could do nothing for her unless I could convince her that she was using her defect as a shield. In fact, she used it both as a shield and as a weapon, to dominate others. She was naturally cantankerous, holding my eyes angrily when I would not look away while she gagged over a word. I thought she would be happier – and this was all I wanted for any of my patients, not increased efficiency, but happiness – if I could make her less frightened of approaching other people as an equal. At present she was always the slighted superior.

I had expected that it would be hard to persuade her of her

own ambivalent attitude towards the stammer, to see that only a small part of her mind, though enough to bring her to the Clinic, was anxious to be rid of it. But this proved simple: she had more intelligence than I had supposed; I became hopeful for her.

What took longer was to make her believe that something worth-while could now be undertaken.

I said, 'Look, there are two ways of coping with your particular variety of trouble. We've tried one and it wouldn't work because you wouldn't let it. We'll start on the second right away. Dorfmeyer's. The first stage will probably seem to you pretty silly, but you've got to get through that to come to the main treatment. Give me a word, any word which normally stops you, and I'll stick on that, doing exactly what you do when you gag, till you release me by saying, "Go on," or "Right," or anything you like, and then I'll finish it. You study just how you stammer.'

The beginning of Dorfmeyer is usually very popular with patients: it reduces the therapist to looking a fool, gives the other person power, and is occasionally the first step on the long road of realisation, by the patient, that if the stammerer can release the therapist, without much effort, the therapist can equally well release the patient, eventually. After this, progress is possible. She kept me gagging on 'page' and then 'programme' for longer than she generally did herself.

I stole a quarter of an hour, unwillingly, from my next appointment, and the violinist was laughing when she left me.

The second patient was someone for whom I had strong personal affection, an eighty year old aphasic who had been coming every week for six months. In that time I had been able to do very little for her, beyond bringing back half a dozen words which she had forgotten, through living alone: but she liked coming for a nice, rambling chat, and I hoped I should be half as spry and jolly if I lived to her age, which luck forbid.

12

I apologised for keeping her waiting, and she said that was all right, she had spent the time thinking out something she wanted to tell me. I heard all over again what a much better Coronation King George V had than the present Queen: for one thing, the rain had held off. Always did, in those days, for royal functions. It struck me with dismay that if I left, probably no-one would bother to go on seeing Mrs. Galloway, since there was nothing more to be achieved with her, professionally.

After her came a man pulling round, better than anyone had expected, from a stroke. Cerebral haemorrhage patients were nearly always a speech-therapist's favourites: it was possible to do more for them, in a shorter time, than for anyone else, teaching them to talk again and watching with pleasure, their pleasure in becoming comprehensible once more.

The last patient of the morning was a small boy with a rare form of dislalia. He knew what he meant to say, he had enough words with which to express it, but more often than not, the idea and the verbal clothing of the idea would not come together. Sounds were difficult for him to copy: he was not tone-deaf, but could not reproduce what he heard. He was brought by a voluble mother whom, as usual, I wanted to strangle.

'Say "Good morning" to the lady, Don. Tell her what you said at breakfast about the cat. He said it beautifully, didn't you, Donald? She won't let you play with those animals if you don't say – '

'Mrs. Latimer, *please* – !'

'But it's not as if he can't say "Good morning," because he said it only a while back to his Dad.'

'I'm not his Dad. More of a stranger.'

'Well, I like that. When I've taken all these mornings off to bring him here.'

We played word-games on the 'Snap!' principle, naming

little plastic animals which I brought out one by one, hidden in my hand, from a drawer behind my back. I let him win toffee from me as a prize, when he named three in succession before I did. At nearly every visit he also won, unofficially, a little animal, and had once got away with two. He was rather a stupid boy, apart from his aural dissociation which made him appear duller than he was, but he was on the way to becoming an accomplished thief. Try as I would I could not keep pairs of animals intact for the game, which he adored. In speech, his progress was slow, but perceptible.

He always left me with a fervent, sticky kiss. I think it was while hugging me that he stretched round into the drawer. That morning, I was in no mood to let him break up another pair of horses which I had recently bought, and I unwrapped the model from his clutch as he made towards the door.

'Oh, Don! Say you're sorry to the lady. You wait till I tell your father. I never knew him do anything like that before. Say –'

'Mrs. Latimer, *please*!!! Now, Don, this week, you just practise talking to the couple of horses you've already got, will you? "One horse, two horses. One horse, two horses." Then next week, maybe there'll be more toffee. "One horse, two hor*ses*".'

With luck, I might get his articulation clear enough to let him, when he grew up, hold down a job in the country, working for a farmer or market gardener. His mother said that with everything that grew: flowers and birds and beasts, he was good and gentle. If not, his only other aptitude would probably shape his life. With luck, and time. If only I could be sure of time!

Because of the extra quarter of an hour spent on the violinist, which I failed to make up during the morning, I was late coming in to the weekly staff lunch, a peculiar Clinic institution which combined food, of a sort, with an opportunity to discuss problems connected with our work, as it

14

affected other members of the staff. Matron beamed on me as I excused myself, but our Almoner glowered.

In the hospital world it was a tradition that Matrons were tough and Almoners sweet, but in this establishment, which at the moment I loved with all my heart, Matron was a charmer and a darling, and the Almoner a grim woman before whom even senior surgeons behaved like nervous students. She was also some close relation to the Chairman of the Board, which gave her special authority. She had made it plain that she had no use for speech-therapists, and at least one speech-therapist had – normally – no use for her, though I had never dared to show this. Today, I appreciated even the characteristic quality of the food. It was the Almoner's boast that, unlike the staffs of many medical foundations, we enjoyed the same meals as the patients in the paying wing. How sick people managed to keep the stuff down I could never imagine.

Unpunctuality annoyed her, and she was sitting opposite me. While I was exploring some muscular stew for an edible piece of meat she leant forward and said, 'One of your patients kept you a very long time this morning.' She noticed every-thing. 'She came straight to me about her travel vouchers after leaving you, and when I saw her it was close on eleven o'clock. Hadn't you another patient at 10.30? Old Mrs. Galloway's day, isn't it? Not that we can do much for her, poor soul. Didn't she come?'

'Yes, she was there, and she waited. The first patient hap-pened to need a bit more time this morning.' I thought, 'I know what comes next!' Usually there were few things I found more exasperating than realising beforehand what the Almoner was about to say, and then waiting to hear her bring out the words. At this lunch I should have been gravely dis-appointed if she had not said them.

'Doesn't do to be too soft with people.' Good, it had come: I would make sure of the next part.

'No, perhaps not,' I prompted vaguely.

15

'You get no thanks for it.' There, it was said.

I intended to answer with something else as non-committal as 'Perhaps not.' But it occurred to me that if I had to lose all this, or might have to lose it, here was the moment for making the loss as worth-while as possible. In minor matters, such as the Almoner's opinion of me, I could be reckless with worry. And I had wanted to say something of the kind for a long time. ('Now, Clo – !') I leant forward, too, enunciating so that my voice might carry all round the table. 'Why should anyone expect to be thanked, for being "too soft" with people?'

'Why should – ?' She stared at me. So did everyone else. Talk ceased momentarily. 'I don't know what you mean.'

'If people choose to be what you call "too soft" with others, that's their affair, isn't it? Why should they want to be thanked for something they choose to do?'

'Mrs. Freeborn, are you feeling quite well?'

'No,' I said, 'I have a headache. I've had it all the morning. But that's got no bearing on what I'm saying.' (It had, of course.) 'Which is this – You've pointed out that it doesn't do to be too soft with people, because you get no thanks for it. You've said that before, too. Well, I can't see why you should get thanks. In fact, I can't –'

Matron, interrupting, twittered to my defence, claiming that we were all liable to headaches, because of the horrid quality of the new strip-lighting, which she personally found very worrying to the eyes – and then we were safely away on to one of our favourite discussion points: what could be done to improve the modern lighting system which had just been installed, at great expense, to everyone's dissatisfaction?

After this Clive Haslett, our visiting ear, nose and throat consultant, produced another reliable topic, co-ordination. Matron talked on soothingly about compromise, linking this with the report problem, and occasionally shooting worried glances towards my side of the table. Naturally she deplored

16

ruffled feelings among the staff. We must all give a point or two to gain a point or two – that was what compromise meant, wasn't it? No-one imagined that busy people, at the end of a long day's work, enjoyed writing out detailed accounts of what might seem to them routine matters. But on the other hand, everyone ought to accept the fact that a new consultant on a case could hardly be expected to read between the lines of a laconic official report, well enough to gather how the patient had responded to previous treatment. All this was calculated to make me feel smug: I was known to be particularly conscientious about these inter-departmental memos. A speech-therapist had to be, to get any co-operation at all.

One of the dental people hazarded the suggestion that we were none of us perfect, in this or any other matter, and for a second or two the Almoner included him in her cold stare. The dental people came low in the hierarchy, and were not expected to open their mouths uninvited, at staff lunch, save to put in food, unless the conversation took a turn which directly affected them. We had some more about compromise in general, in a chat between Matron and one of the resident doctors. Were the British not supposed to have a genius for it? For instance, there was Churchill during the war, acting as a good friend to the Communists, whose policies he detested, and saying, 'Anyone who fights Nazis is my ally.' One simply had to compromise a bit, all the time, to get anywhere. 'Well, now, on your bikes, girls and boys!' This was one of the House-Surgeon's favourite jokes, as if we were a youth club stopping at a wayside café. I should have been sorry if that had not come.

The afternoon was uneventful. I took a heavy chaser-dose of aspirin, the first, in the morning, having had no effect, and at last the headache lifted. Two of my patients failed to keep their appointments. They were small children, who should have been brought by their mothers. They were often late, anyway, and as no word was sent that for once they were not going to turn up at all, by the time I realised this it was too late to see anyone else instead. This sort of thing happened frequently with the free service; never, of course, or hardly ever, with paying patients. If they neither appeared, nor got a message through to me, it was safe to assume that some quite serious emergency had intervened. I reminded myself that what I had said at lunch, mainly to annoy the Almoner, was incidentally true. If I had no right to expect thanks, because it was pleasanter to be soft than hard, then I also had no right to get angry when I was treated without consideration. My time at the Clinic was paid for by public funds: if the public chose not to use it, that was the public's affair; but I wished mothers were not so easily discouraged by bus journeys, washing-day, or the sheer boredom of taking their children anywhere regularly. Eventually, when I had stopped expecting them, I got on with the writing of reports – those handing-on reports, about speech-defectives who should have an I.Q. test, and also needed their adenoids removed – which Clive Haslett had complained were rarely co-ordinated properly. But then he was talking of reports from other people's departments. His and mine worked together admirably; there were reasons for that.

When I left, at six, I passed his door as I went along the corridor. Desolately, I longed to see him alone, if only for a moment, to tell him what was happening, or likely to happen, at home. He was working late, judging by the reflection of his desk-lamps streaming out through the fanlight above the door. He usually did, on the one day a week when our time at the Clinic overlapped. And on other days, too, I knew. He was a very good and completely dedicated doctor. We never talked, in this place, except on official matters. We had come together before I worked here, and I had heard, through him, of the vacant post for a speech-therapist, and had applied for it successfully.

Outside, we could rarely meet for more than a few minutes

except by elaborate contrivance. Catching the train by which I was expected home left little time after the last of my day's appointments, and his. We could sit in a teashop and talk, occasionally, and that was all. But we were lovers when the chance came, and had been for a long time.

I thought of knocking on his door, and if necessary – if anyone else happened to be there – making a Clinic excuse: those reports. We shared several patients whom he had sent to me in the first place. But the schooling of years was too strong. I had told myself so often. Make no demands. Efface yourself. These are the only terms on which you can keep your lover. This gifted, vulnerable lover who must at any cost be protected.

Walking on down the corridor I wondered again what small degree of relief would be mixed with his regret if I went away: after all, however careful we were, I remained a menace to his career – rightly (and I accepted this without reservation) more important to him than anything else.

I turned a corner in the ground floor passage, near the front entrance, and met him face to face.

He had been down to the X-ray department for some plates – oblivious of the time, I knew with exasperated affection, and of the possibility of our saying at least good night to one another if he had been ready to leave when I had to go, or miss my train. We were not likely to be able to meet during the following week.

So it would have been useless to knock: irrationally, I was glad that I had kept some control, and angry with myself because this chance meeting could bring the blood into my face wildly enough to make me afraid of anyone happening to come by.

'Clo, what got into you at lunch?'

'I – well, I don't know'. It was impossible to tell him here, with other feet approaching from the further side of the blind corner. If my husband accepted the job in Hong Kong, I should have no choice but to go with him. To refuse would be to make positive in his mind the suspicion which I believed was already there. And this I could not afford, for Clive.

'You'll have the old bitch on your tracks for ever after this!'

'Angels and Ministers of Grace defend me!' I said, and laughed, and hurried on. The feet were nearing the corner.

In fact, the Almoner never made another comment on the running of my schedules for the rest of my time at the Clinic.

CHAPTER III

Conversation

MY HUSBAND WAS already home when I arrived.

'Well?' I said, my back turned, taking off my coat. He had asked me not to telephone to his office during the day to find out if any decision had been made yet. Too many ears might be listening.

'Well, what?'

How Barney enjoyed small power, I thought, making me ask to know my fate.

'Do we go out East?'

'Yes.'

'Oh. Congratulations. It means promotion for you in a big way, doesn't it? When do we go?'

'Probably in about three months.'

'As soon as that? We shall have to get busy, selling off furniture and anything we don't want to take with us.'

'Everything depends on the staff out there finding us reasonable accommodation. And that's terribly scarce, as I expect

20

you know. You must have heard about the overcrowding in Hong Kong?'

'Oh, I have. Yes.'

'Obviously, we can't go till they've got us somewhere to live. That's easier for Europeans, who have some money, than for refugees, who mostly haven't any. But flats are harder to come by than houses, I'm told – it was different when I was there before – and everything's in short supply at the price we'd be prepared to pay. I'm not going to be bled by any landlord taking advantage of the situation to charge something quite monstrous. I've written that to the man I'm replacing. Unfortunately, he isn't coming home. He's retiring and staying on out there, so we can't simply inherit his house.'

'I see.'

'You're taking this very calmly.'

'No. Not really. Not inside. It's just – I'm shocked, I think.'

' "Shocked"?' he said, puzzled. A good man, he was frequently shocked himself by cruelty, by gross self-seeking, by injustice, if it happened to be towards people in the mass, in categories: the coloured, or some particular persecuted sect. He was not so easily moved, I had found, by evil treatment of individuals.

'Oh, shocked in the medical sense, of course,' I said irritably, thinking how strange it was that at such a time I could be annoyed by a simple misunderstanding over a word. Barney and I brought out the worst in one another. 'I'm very glad for you. Sorry about my work here.'

'You won't need to work,' he told me with satisfaction. 'Counting in our living allowance, my salary will be almost doubled.'

I opened my mouth to say something, and could find nothing to say, and so busied myself providing us with a drink apiece, to celebrate his getting what he had wanted, I knew, for a long time. Because he had a complicated self-thwarting quality in him, which made him instinctively step back when worldly wisdom would have urged him to step forward, he had twice been passed over for a branch managership in the Import-Export firm where he had been assistant manager for too long.

Was it possible that by now he had forgotten how I had fought for my training, for my chance to work, after our son died, six years ago? Perhaps. No-one could ever be sure of the limits of another human being's ability to forget at will. Come to that, who knew his or her own power, in this direction? I looked at him carefully, and through him at myself, as we raised our glasses and smiled.

Here was a man whom I had once believed that I could make happy, or at least happier. I must have believed that, I thought wonderingly, or surely I should not have married him, not even at a time in my life when I badly needed to do something for somebody. And since then I had failed him. I had not managed, as cleverer wives did with their husbands, to make him feel important, and convince him that I looked up to him for his many real excellencies of character. I recognised that he was a much nicer and better person than I was. Unfortunately this is not endearing knowledge.

'Cheers! Here's to the new life,' I said.

After a few minutes, he refilled our glasses. In the ordinary way we had one stiff drink each, to rule a line under the day's stint, before I started cooking our evening meal, prepared beforehand by the charwoman. But this was an occasion.

We had married shortly after the war, both of us as a reaction from other loves which had ended sadly. The girl he ought to have had died in a German concentration camp. In our earlier days together, when I still minded that I could occupy only a little of his heart, I surmised, in mean moments, that it was because she was of Jewish blood, one of a beleaguered minority, that he had fallen in love with her, and remained in love with her.

And my man had been killed not even as a direct result of

22

the war but in a senseless, unnecessary car-accident, from which I had escaped with a small scar on the chin – something I could never bring myself to have obliterated. Indeed, it was all that remained for me of that first, very young love, born of the excitement and stimulus of the time. We were no more than interested strangers when he died. He had never mattered to my heart, as Clive mattered now. Pity on both sides, a blind seeking for comfort, had been the motive behind Barney's and my marriage, and pity had not been enough.

As he gave my glass back to me he said awkwardly, 'I'm glad you're coming with me, Chloe. I was afraid you might decide not to.'

Panic swept over me: somehow, then, he knew – he must know – about Clive. Despite all our care, someone had talked.

For a few suffocating seconds I thought of throwing myself on his kindness, of admitting everything and asking him, as I had asked him once before, to let me go, without recrimination. But it would be to his mercy towards another man, not towards me, that I should have to appeal now. I knew enough of his uprightness, of his tortuous regard for truth (prompted by – what? Something more human, I thought, which he would never recognize), to be almost sure that if he were certain Clive had been my lover, he would insist on naming him in the divorce court. I could hear Barney's clear, precise voice saying, 'I am not going to lie in this matter. That's final.' And he would take the same course if he knew that Clive's wife would never let her husband go, on religious grounds, though they no longer lived together. He would damage Clive with the best motives, to no purpose for anyone.

I put all the warmth and surprise I could into my voice. 'What a funny thing to say! All day, waiting to hear, I've never even considered not coming.' That, at least, was true.

'No? Good.' He was prepared to say nothing further, but I must know more, if I could.

'What made you say that?' Yes, paying close attention to

my voice, I could be satisfied with its sound of innocence. This was the miserable, demeaning part of a liaison, the lying and acting it required. And yet when Clive and I could be together, it seemed such a small price to pay.

'Remember two years ago?'

'Oh, that!' I said, enormously relieved. 'But that was – well – two years ago.'

Two years ago, just before I met Clive, I had tried to make my husband see that our association had become quite meaningless, and to agree to a friendly break. But to him marriage was marriage, though he was not a Catholic like Clive's wife, and he had refused. There could be no amiable collusion. He had asked, 'What reason have you got for leaving me?' and I said, 'We bring out the worst in one another.' It seemed to me then – it still seemed to me – the best possible reason for ending a partnership of any kind. I made him more self-righteous: and my reaction to his high seriousness, and his – at times – extraordinarily insensitive goodness, was to become petty and spiteful, against my will.

'I don't think I ever heard a sillier reason,' he had told me then. 'Because after all, how other people affect you is one of the few things entirely within your own control,' and the appeal was ignored.

'Well, I'm glad you haven't gone on feeling the same, all this time!' he said now. 'Let's have supper.' And I could not decide in my own mind how much or how little he knew.

Compromise – retreating, little by little, from one defensive position to another, till there was really nothing left to defend. Matron was quite wrong, I thought – dear, understanding soul that she was – in holding that this was how you achieved anything. You fought hard for the success of a marriage, giving way a little here and a little there, because you must; and presently you found yourself still striving, for something that was no longer worth the fight. Perhaps all wars were like that: big wars, in which men began struggling

24

for freedom, and ended by fastening a new slavery on other men: and little wars, between two human beings unsuitably tied together. You compromised, losing bit by bit your bright, clear apprehension of an ideal, and presently you could hardly remember what it was you had once believed in, staunchly.

'Spaghetti with eggs, or cheese, or both?' I called back from the kitchen, and cooked what he chose with unusual care. Meticulous about my work outside, I inclined to be slapdash in the house.

During the meal, because silence between us was often oppressive, I asked, 'Did you play liar-dice when you were in the Navy?'

'Oh, yes, any amount of it. We got very keen on it in Scapa.'

'As a consolation for not being able to do the things you'd enjoyed in civilian life?'

'Well, possibly. I remember hating not being able to read anything that needed concentration, while we were at sea, because of the constant interruptions. And thinking I'd make up for it when I got the chance. And then I didn't. Nobody did, even when we were hanging about shore establishment, waiting for demobilisation, with all the time in the world. We just played liar-dice in the mess.'

'That's more or less what I meant. Something you do to fill up an emptiness in yourself, coming to matter more, eventually, than the emptiness, or the cause of it.'

'What's started you thinking about liar-dice?'

'Man I met in the train this morning. Someone I hadn't seen since I was in Belgium. He pulled out a photograph of himself and some others playing liar-dice: he just happened to have the picture on him. No, I think probably he always carries it about. You know how absurdly moving old snapshots are, even trivial ones. He has a son with a stammer – '

'Oh. Has he?' Barney quickly grew bored with talk about

separate cases, though patients as a broad division of humanity could be interesting.

'The boy may come to me at the Clinic,' I finished, and silence came back.

Barney washed up for me after supper, refusing to let me help; knowing, he said, that I must have had an exhausting day, with the anxiety of waiting for the news on top of my work. He was often very nice about practical things.

'You'll like having Chinese servants,' he suggested, coming back into the living room when the chores were done. 'Everyone agrees, they're excellent.'

'Yes, I expect I shall.' Servants in exchange for love.

As things were, we considered ourselves lucky to have secured a charwoman for two hours a day. I was hardly ever in the house while she was there, to keep an eye on her work, and in the circumstances, it was not too bad.

'We'll probably get a man and his wife, living in. After all, in Hong Kong, if more than a million people have come across the Chinese border illegally, there ought to be no labour shortage. I expect we'll have to entertain a good deal.'

'I'll like that, too.' (Would I?) 'But I thought that would be rather against your principles – two able-bodied people doing nothing but look after two other able-bodied people. You've always been a bit scornful about that sort of employment-ratio.'

'It's somewhat different when there are masses and masses of people desperately looking for any kind of work at all! For them, there's practically no kind of employment that isn't better than none. I'm hoping to be free in my spare time, which is one of the reasons for having servants, to do some social welfare work. That's if I get any free time from the job: I don't suppose I shall, at first. I expect you'll want to take up something of the same kind. They must need any amount of voluntary helpers, with that fantastic crowd of destitute

26

people pouring in. Very fascinating, the whole political and economic set-up.'

'Yes. It's bound to be.'

We went to bed, and I still could not tell, then or ever, how much he had guessed or been told about Clive.

CHAPTER IV

Hay along the Hedges

CLIVE WAS CHARMING in every way – understanding, affectionate, and deeply concerned for me – when at last I was able to give him the news.

No hint of this showed on the surface if he knew a moment of ambivalent thankfulness: the decision to break off this association, dangerous only for him, had been taken out of our hands. It would have seemed perfectly comprehensible to me if he had felt that: comprehensible, but, of course, not warming. He was delightful.

He made a tremendous effort of successful organization, to get us a whole day in the country by ourselves. It was the day when, once every three weeks, I was supposed to spend my official hours visiting the homes of my younger patients, to see for myself their backgrounds. (Many retarded children are reported by schools to be in need of therapy for faulty word-co-ordination, when in fact they belong to families where speech is hardly used at all for communication. Treatment is unnecessary, and would be useless. At the age of six or seven they have not heard enough words to be able to put them round the simplest idea, beyond 'Gimme – ') Normally, this was my most valuable and productive day, helping me to decide on methods to use, or the modification of what had already been started: and nothing would make me give it up. But it was the one day when I need not account for my time to anyone. I sacrificed it without a qualm.

As if to punish me, everything in the smiling, late-June countryside seemed to be a conspiracy to make it as hard as possible for me to leave England. The cuckoo called its double note, the only satisfying stammer in nature: brambles caught at my feet, holding me back, when we walked through a copse festooned with wild roses. It was the season for hay-lifting, early that year after a long, fine spell, and wisps hung on the hedges, where the carts had passed. Love was in everything we saw, everything we touched.

He raged against the necessity of my going; against Barney's assumption, when Hong Kong was first mentioned between us, that if a husband were promoted, the wife, whatever her commitments, should be expected to follow wherever that promotion led; against the world's underlying attitude towards women's work outside the home, which still put this on a level with painting in water colours by Victorian ladies – something to be dropped at once if a man wanted anything. 'What nonsense this makes of the lip-service paid to equality in these days! You, Clo, are a valuable speech-therapist. An instinctive one, which is rare: you're not just well trained. If you hadn't long eyelashes I should still want to send my patients to you. And your husband is about to become – what is it? Branch manager of some trading company, isn't it? And nobody but me, I suppose, would think it idiotic that you should give up your job for his, instead of the other way round. And I'm biased, of course.'

'I daresay imports and exports are a lot more valuable to the country as a whole than speech-therapy,' I said. 'And anyway, my darling, let's not talk about that any more. Because we both know this isn't why I'm going – what Barney or the world expects from a wife in the way of "Pay, pack and follow." If you, Dr. Haslett, met a set-back through me, you would be very, very considerate about it at the time – we both know that, too. And later, you'd resent it bitterly, and I'd resent your resentment. Let's not waste time trying to change what we can't. Let's enjoy today.'

Strangely, we did, or most of it.

The following day Paul's son appeared at the Clinic for the first time, coming by himself with a note from the school doctor which was far too brief. It told me nothing about the boy's general condition. Taller and fairer than his father, he was a thin, unsmiling lad of fifteen, with an exceptionally bad stammer of the convulsive blocking type – a variety which is often more painful to the onlooker than the sufferer.

His father's aggressiveness seemed to have doubled itself in him, which was rather what I expected. There is an extreme, psycho-medical school of thought which holds that in the strong connection between aggressiveness and stammering, it is the aggressiveness which is the cause, and the speech-defect the result; not the other way round. By this theory, the stammerer is venting on the world, through making it uncomfortable while listening to the struggle for expression, envy, hatred and malice galore. I thought this was whimsical nonsense; but it was truer than any demonstrable truth to the German colleague whose assistant I had been before I came to the Clinic. This boy seemed to back up his belief.

I was aware from the start that the battle of wills between therapist and patient, inevitable at the beginning of treatment for his particular trouble, was going to be prolonged beyond the usual period of stress.

Uncertain if I had time enough for the treatment to be of any use to him, but wanting to live only for the moment, not to look forward, I flung myself into fighting for him, and, at first, into fighting the lad himself.

'I have to put down a few details,' I said, getting out an official form. 'First, will you tell me your name?'

No audible answer. He blocked on the first syllable, eyeing me balefully, willing me to look away, as he could nearly always make the rest of his world do, either from pity or impatience.

'You see, I know your father's first name, because as I expect he told you, we met long ago, one day during the war. And that was a time, if you were in any of the Services' – I was talking deliberately slowly, amiably, holding his eyes, robbing him of his sorry victory – 'you knew hundreds and hundreds of other Service people by their first names, but very often you never got – '

'Johnny – ' he blurted out.

' – never got their other names at all. So I know your father's called Paul, but not what your surname is.' In fact, it was mentioned in the doctor's note, Hamilton: but pretended ignorance was safe enough. The letter had come sealed, inside another sealed envelope.

I went on waiting: I could feel hostility to the imperturbable watcher building up in him.

'Do you like to be called Johnny or John?' I asked, when he began banging my table with one hand.

He shook his head over 'John' and banged on, not trying to stare me down any more for the moment but looking over my head, darting glances at me to see if I minded the noise, at least.

'All right, Johnny, then. Try doing that with both hands. Sometimes it helps.'

Sometimes it could, but only through the accident that on some occasion a blocked word had released itself while the stammerer was making a rhythmic movement, tapping or banging, and success had become associated with the movement.

'Jo – Jo – ' He would not use both hands because I had suggested it, almost in the form of an order.

'Why go back to "Johnny"? You've said that. It's always a

30

pity to go back to a word that stuck, after you've managed to unstick it. Waste of time and breath and energy, don't you see? Go straight ahead. Your father's Paul – what? And so you're Johnny – what?'

'Hamilton,' he got out, on an indrawn breath, a little to my surprise. I thought he would insist on going through 'Johnny' again, having begun to back-track. He stopped banging then and told me with only a catch here and there that he was not coming again. He had only shown up today because his Dad had said I was a funny one. Talked a lot of rot. And they had given him the afternoon off from school to come.

'You don't like school? Do they laugh at your stammer there? The other boys?'

This he would not answer, replying instead, getting the aspirate easily on a half-breath, 'Who says I don't like – ' and then blocking.

Here was a possible line of progress: I should be able to help him towards better control of breathing. Before I went any further with the case, I ought to have a psychiatrist's report on his intelligence, and some information from his headmaster, but by the nature of their trouble, their desperate lack of confidence, stammerers tended to come miserably out of official reports and I.Q. tests; also I had very little faith in the eminent mental consultant attached to the clinic: I would take a chance by going on without a report, assuming a fair degree of intelligence.

'You said yourself you didn't like school. Well, as good as said it, a minute ago. You told me you didn't want to come here, but they gave you the afternoon off from school for it. If coming here and listening to me talking rot is better than being at school, you can't think much of school. You know, I think the boys jeer at you when you stammer. I think they copy you doing it. Don't they?'

Unless I drove this home, without mercy if necessary, he was almost certainly going to take the line that he had never

31

cared whether he stammered or not, which would make any treatment more difficult. Once an attitude had been struck it would be particularly hard for this lad to give it up.

'Don't they?' I said.

They better not. He could floor anyone his weight. In the school boxing – He began to boast, but the stammer returned and spoilt it.

'The chaps you knock down can still laugh at you when they get up, though.' With a twisted heart I saw that this thought had gone through the pathetic armour.

What would we do, if he came, he asked sullenly.

Each exchange between us took several minutes, but I could use the time to watch for inconsistencies and special anxieties.

'Get you interested in your stammer.' He made a derisory noise. 'You'd be interested as soon as you found out what makes you stammer – and when – and how to cope with it. I can see you've already noticed for yourself, you're better off with some words when you're breathing in than when you're breathing out.'

He was not interested, he said – rather well, taking the tip and inhaling as he spoke.

'Then you're just a fool,' I said, facing the big risk. To be laughed at – to be mocked in any way – must be agony to this boy. 'You're like a general who has the chance to learn all about his enemy – where he can hit him hardest – and simply can't be bothered. What a fool!'

'You do talk a lot of rot,' he said, after a great deal of difficulty, hating me again, trying to make me avert my eyes from the long gagging on the 'r' of 'rot'.

'So do you, if I may say so!' I told him. 'Only I can do it without stammering. But then so could you, if you knew how.'

'What else would we do?'

I had decided quickly, on the nervous symptoms which went with the worst gagging, to try a modified van Riper approach. The trouble with van Riper was that it called for considerable understanding on the part of the patient. How much co-operation could I get? I was Authority, like the school, like his father, and he was hostile to these things. How badly Paul must have handled him! I could hardly imagine his father treating anyone with imagination or sympathy, but this unyielding lad least of all.

'What else? Plenty more. Too complicated to go right through now. It's a whole process, you see. One bit would be, you'd talk to yourself, watching yourself in a mirror.'

He would look a proper Charlie, he objected contemptuously.

'But you'd soon talk more like a proper Johnny.' No smile came in reply; instead, a complete irrelevancy, persisted in to the end of the sentence with revealing determination. His Dad said I had a scar on my chin and so I had. Where did I g –

He blocked completely and I would not help, but sat there impassively meeting his look, resisting his desire to dominate.

Suddenly he picked up that point of avoiding backtracking, and allied it to careful breathing. ' – get it?' I began to hope that he was teachable, like the violinist. He would forget, of course: he forgot even this simple first advance several times in the course of the first interview, but unless in a specially obstinate phase, he could be gently reminded, and then go forward again, or try to, wholeheartedly.

'This is the souvenir of a car-accident. You see, I didn't only meet your father during the war. I met a lorry head-on.' He gave a thin smile, the first since he came in. He began tapping soundlessly with both hands on his knee, below the level of the table between us, but I could see the slight movement of the upper arms: he enunciated admirably, 'J. for Johnny,' and then made a grimace, sneering at me, or himself, or both.

'Oh, well done,' I exclaimed, off guard: it was essential he should have at least one success in loosening up at this initial interview.

He turned sulky at once. I was not to think he was coming again. What he'd do, he explained, was this: he'd get time off, all right, but he knew better ways of spending it! I noted with interest, for possible further investigation, that he spoke with a much broader Cockney accent than his father. The influence of a mother-substitute, perhaps? If so, she might be important.

'Suppose you'd ring up the school and tell if I wasn't here?' This sentence took great labour to produce. By the time he ended it he was hot and disgusted with me for the presumed sneaking.

'No, I wouldn't, Johnny. Get this straight. It doesn't make any difference to me if you come or not. As I told your father, there's no charge, it's part of the Health Service that I'm paid to sit here whatever you choose to do. If you make an appointment and don't keep it, what happens? I get a nice bit of free time to myself. That's all. See?'

Obviously he had no wish to give me this benefit. Pushing the advantage, I said, 'If you do decide to come – next Thursday, same time – you ought to do a bit of homework between now and then.'

No. He was not going to do any homework. Too much like school.

'Then don't come. Because there's no sense in turning up a second time if you haven't prepared for it. All you have to do is to write down ten words you've stuck over, during the week. The exact words. Not the sentences they came in, just the difficult words. And grin when you write them down. This bit's important, even if it doesn't sound so to you. Grin hard, over each one. Show your teeth at it.'

We practised baring our teeth at one another: he was not averse from this.

'Ever tried using the telephone?' I asked.

What did I think – he was barmy or something? The fear of being laughed at – 'got at' he called it – made him offensive once more.

34

I chose to understand what he managed to say in the way he did not intend: that of course, at his age, he was accustomed to the telephone.

'Good. I thought you knew your way about. Well, here's my private phone number, I'll write it down for you. It'll only get me in the evenings, after about 7.15. I want you to let me know, by phone, before you come – if you do – which are the ten words you've written down because they caught when you tried to say them. That'll help me to plan the next tackle. And please grin when you tell me. I don't care how long it takes to get out the words. You can grin till your face aches. Use a call-box so you'll be by yourself. No-one else listening or watching. Here are the four pennies. You know, you can hear a grin on the phone. In the voice.'

He made the jeering noise again.

'You can, really, Johnny. I'll show you, by doing it back, when you phone. Of course, I just might happen to be out the evening you choose to phone, but if so, please try again, the next night. Anyway, before this day week. Is there a public phone-box near your home?'

He didn't know, and anyway, had other plans for his evenings. But he took the four pennies and the number, got up abruptly and left without saying goodbye.

I found that my light summer blouse was sticking to my skin, though it was quite cool weather – not like the lovely preceding day when Clive and I had lain together, with sprays of wild roses above us.

The Almoner's words came back into my mind. It was just as well not to want thanks for loving one's job, since thanks were rarely forthcoming.

I had never had such a sense of personal responsibility for a patient before. If, years ago, I had run off my patter slower, or more convincingly to Paul on Melbroek airfield, the boy might not have had a broken home, nor his present crippling disability. He would still have been inclined to develop some slight speech-defect – a full-blown stammer never came from insecurity alone: a nervous weakness must have been there in his early childhood – but it need not have been something which now cut him off from human friendship more effectively than if he had been blind or maimed. He was so unlike his father to look at that probably he had taken strongly after his mother. This could not have eased the difficult relationship.

The evenings passed and no telephone call came from Johnny, but I was fairly confident that he would turn up at any rate once more, if only out of curiosity, or to try staring me down again, or merely for the relief of being away from school in the company of someone apparently indifferent as to whether he stammered or not.

In the meantime Barney told me, with exasperation, that there seemed likely to be a long delay over getting us a house or a flat in Hong Kong. 'I've had two letters in three days about it. I've already let them know out there I'm willing to live over in Kowloon and commute by ferry. Crossing the harbour only takes about ten minutes each way. Of course, it wouldn't be as pleasant as living on the island itself, if possible half way up the Peak. But anything's better than hanging about indefinitely, now we know we're going.'

He had known Hong Kong for three months, roughly at the time when I was stationed at Melbroek. The Japanese had just left. To crews coming ashore from British ships in the harbour, it must have seemed a spacious place: I could see that Barney suspected someone was being inefficient and slack about our housing problem.

'Still, it's easy to criticize when one isn't there,' he said fairly. 'I suppose things must be in a mess. I hear that several of the big banks started building hostels to house their staffs, several years ago. I wish our firm had thought of doing that in time.'

'Yes, it would have helped,' I said, not bothering to express

36

my views on hostel life in my thankfulness for the reprieve. Perhaps it would go on and on. I decided that no-one at the clinic except Clive need know as yet that I was going.

I became more optimistic than usual in my reports on dubious cases referred to me at the Clinic for the decision, was this patient likely to benefit from speech-therapy or not? For very old people, after more than one stroke, and also for borderline mental cases with marked dissociation, treatment could be worse than a waste of everyone's energy: it became a strain on the tired mind or body, asked to put forth an effort no longer possible. It meant, too, that the therapist would have less time to spend on responsive cases: official hours could not be endlessly elastic. But I always shrank from giving the verdict that no attempt should be made. Surely, however decrepit and scarcely human a man or woman had become, it was invaluable to re-learn one word, 'yes' or 'no', for however short a time, rather than be shut living, sooner than need be, into a world of silence. I always wanted to try, and now more than ever.

Against my better judgement I took on several new patients, both at the Clinic and privately, for whom the results achieved were probably quite negligible compared with the demand I made of them, and the work I put into doing it: but I managed to go to bed every night too exhausted to think very much.

'You'll knock yourself out at this rate,' Barney said, with what I thought was a certain relish. 'For your own sake I'll be thankful when you have to give up this over-driving. Women in jobs either seem to be without any conscience at all, like our typists who take far more than their lunch-hour, every day, or they're your sort. Bullied by a sense of duty.'

'I don't do anything I do from a sense of duty. That's your speciality! And sweeping generalisations about men and women – '

I stopped because I realised he was not listening. The post had arrived, and Barney was eagerly tearing open a large

37

packet. It was just as well that I broke off in mid-sentence: my temper was sharpening under stress. Over the years my attitude towards my husband had become apologetic. 'I'm sorry' or 'My fault' I said rather too often, in trivial matters: but not in this waiting period. It was one thing to take the right decision, the only possible decision, but quite another, unhappily, to carry it out in a decent, equable manner. I had been going to say something calculated to hurt him where he was most vulnerable, in his pride in his own judgement, always independent of the popular view.

Later, when habit reasserted itself and I tried to make amends for my edginess, the excuse I chose for overworking to this seemingly pointless degree was that I wanted to round off my job in style. It was a reason which Barney could accept easily.

'Look!' He held up several pamphlets which had come out of the packet. He had sent to the Hong Kong Government Information Service for publications giving the latest figures on overcrowding in the shanty-towns and Chinese owned tenements, where the refugees slept in relays, hiring bed-space for a few hours at a stretch. Some of the photographs included were horrifying. He showed them to me with real understanding and sympathy for a massive human problem.

Late enough to dislocate the whole of my afternoon timetable, Johnny appeared on Thursday, without having telephoned. He had lost my number, he said, his eyes daring me to let him see I knew he was lying. He had not done the other small assignment, either: it was 'stupid.' But he insisted on giving back the four unused pennies.

'Keep them to make the call some time this week,' I suggested, and he almost threw them across the table to me. The grimacing which went with a prolonged block grew worse when he became indignant. He could afford to phone if he wanted to phone. His father gave him more money than most of the other boys had! (This I could easily believe: Paul Hamilton would do it out of unrecognized remorse.)

Then jubilation took over in Johnny; but it did nothing towards freeing his speech. After a long struggle he was able to tell me of his victory. He had made his father agree to his leaving school and taking a job. The battle between them had been long and bitter, Paul Hamilton for once talking sense, as it seemed to me. But the boy was adamant; not to be moved by reasoning or abuse. He had reached the legal school-leaving age. Education could no longer be forced on him, and his future could look after itself, for all he cared. Term ended in a few weeks, and then he would be free.

His father had made the condition of his leaving that the boy must be able to prove that he had the offer of a job of some kind. Paul expected, I imagine, that the stammer would be an insuperable obstacle. But the lad had initiative and drive: the foreman of a local factory had obliged with a grubby chit, which Johnny brought with him and showed me as though it were a prisoner's discharge. Waiting for him was a dead-end job, as a summer holiday replacement in the packing department. The pay, as he was not yet seventeen and a learner, was probably less than his pocket money, but nothing could lessen his satisfaction.

This disastrous move would come hard, I thought, on his father, who had wanted the boy to go on to technical college and train for a degree in some branch of mechanics. Just because he had never had any kind of qualification himself, Johnny told me contemptuously. Paul must once have pinned all his hopes on his son, and been sourly disappointed.

Though I told him I was against his throwing aside all further education, Johnny and I got on together much more peaceably during the whole of this session. We went into situations he feared, such as being asked the way by a stranger in the street. This had only happened once because he had grown wary, but the idea that it might happen was a recur-

39

rent worry. He kept his eyes open and crossed the road, if necessary, when he saw anyone looking about uncertainly.

He volunteered to tell me which letters he believed tried him hardest, but was not very sound on this, having failed to notice that it was less the letter itself than its position in a word which mattered. He could come out with an initial 'P' better than many lesser stammerers, but was helpless when 'P' came after the first syllable. 'Packing' was all right: 'department' took several attempts.

He had returned to back-tracking, which was bad throughout the session, but eased himself out of a block more than once by pounding with both hands, openly now: he could accept my advice occasionally. He seemed less anxious to overbear me into looking away at the worst moments.

Testing his memory, often poor in speech-defectives, and his family attachment at the same time, I asked him if he remembered his mother. 'Your father mentioned there was a break-up between them when you were about three.' I did not know if his parents were actually divorced: probably not, I thought: they were not in a divorcing stratum. 'Break-up' would do.

He remembered nothing, and did not want to remember. 'She was no good.'

'Oh, nonsense,' I said. 'You can't be sure of that. You're old enough to understand that war does a lot of strange things to people.' (I always treated him, and other juveniles, as though they were a year or two beyond the ages marked on their records.) 'Your people were kept apart for years, and she was young, and found another man when your father had been away for a long time. She probably didn't even remember very clearly what he looked like. I don't suppose they'd been married long when he went overseas. Well, thousands of women did just the same, in every country where the men were off fighting somewhere else, or captured, and they weren't all rotten.'

He interrupted me to say that he knew all about women. She was no good.

I let the 'all' pass, he had met enough trouble with 'about'. 'Why do you say that, Johnny?'

He astounded me by asserting, his impediment becoming acute, that he thought he was not his father's son. She had always been 'like that'. Even before the army took his father away.

Wish-fulfilment, I surmised. As a child, I should hardly have fancied Paul Hamilton for a father, myself: better some ideal unknown, who could never hector and trample. But I felt sure that for this boy, a double sense of insecurity and belonging nowhere was not going to help: he, of all young people, could not afford that particular fantasy.

'Just because you don't look like him? Taller and fairer?'

He nodded.

'I'm certain you are his son,' I said. 'You're very much like him in other ways. More important ways.' (Unfortunately!)

He looked stubbornly unbelieving.

I said, 'Wouldn't you agree that I'm medium-height and medium-colour? I can assure you, so's my husband. Perhaps a little darker. But the son we had was very fair, and he looked like growing very tall. And I ought to know, he belonged to both of us.'

Johnny seemed impressed, and brought out one of his queer irrelevancies. 'Where is he? Your son?'

'He isn't anywhere. He's dead.'

He said very carefully, timing his breathing well by the aspirates, 'How d'you know – he isn't anywhere – if he's dead?'

'I don't know, of course,' I told him briskly. 'I just think so. What do you think?'

Johnny said he did not know either, and asked another question about my son, for reassurance. Was he really very much fairer than either of us?

41

'Yes.' It happened so long ago that I could speak of my child's death, now, without emotion, though I preferred not to unless there was some good reason for it. 'But he isn't the person we're here to talk about. We're here to talk about you. I want you to do a mirror exercise for me – ' and suddenly I realised that whichever we talked of, for me we were talking about the same person. For a few seconds the old pain swept back with half-forgotten strength. Physically, not in any way but build and colour and the defencelessness of being very young, Johnny was much what Alan might have been had he lived. Something in my flesh and nerves must have recognized this, before my mind, to make me worry so much whether or not this boy would come again to let me help him.

He disliked the mirror exercise, but did it without looking away, himself, when the grimacing started, at the first block. Most patients with his particular form of stammering needed persuasion to face their ugliness at these moments.

'Will you show me with your finger where you feel the most tension? It's under the chin, isn't it, and at the corners of the mouth?' I was standing behind him, so that we could look into the same hand-mirror, while he held it.

He shook his head, turned, and ran his finger along above my upper lip, and then picked out a spot in each cheek.

'What do you imagine other people think of you when you can't answer them?'

'Think I'm – ' He began to say 'a bit barmy' but changed it to the less difficult 'mad.'

'And what do you think of yourself?'

'Think – I'm mad, too.'

'Well, I don't. I think you're a boy with enough brains to see that if you've got to live with a stammer, you'd better find ways of stopping it making you miserable. I'm not promising to get rid of it altogether, you understand. Only to show you how to control it. Here's one way – ' I started him on breathing exercises combined with speech, while he watched his face to see which set of muscles tightened involuntarily, and then how soon he could induce them to slacken.

When he tired beyond concentration, which was depressingly quickly, I read to him, paraphrasing where necessary, from one of the text-books dealing with the method I had begun to use. How much he took in, I could not be sure: but reading was less personal than talking. I guessed that he could accept from a printed page more than he would be willing as yet to take from me.

'D'you think you could find time to do the mirror exercise several times, by yourself, before next Thursday? Notice ten words you avoid saying, write them down – grinning – and say them to the mirror. After that, telephone them to me.'

He was not coming on Thursday. School boxing tournament. His last. He was not going to miss it.

'The Monday after, then, Johnny? We might get in two visits that week, to make up. Monday and Thursday?'

He turned sullen and managed something vague about everyone always 'going on' at him.

'Is there any other time you'd rather come? Remember I only work here three days a week. Monday, Tuesday, and Thursday.'

He was not coming. Silly, all that grinning. Didn't help.

I explained again, briefly, what the act of smiling did to the jaw muscles. 'All right, don't think of what you do when you're writing down those words as "grinning," if that seems silly to you. I said, "grin" as the simplest way of getting your face to back up your brains and do something that does help. If you like it better that way, take it you're using one set of muscles to stop another set of muscles from doing something to annoy you.'

At this point the discreet bell over my door rang for the second time during the session. This signalled the arrival of the patient due after the patient who followed Johnny. I could not go on arguing. When he left, as before, without saying goodbye, I had no idea if he would come again, or not.

At home, that evening, I got out a photograph of Alan to see if I had been imagining the likeness. No, it was there. This was the picture of a boy much younger than Johnny, but it might have been Johnny, taken years ago. The same snub nose, which freckled: the same wide, thin-lipped mouth. Not a particularly good looking face, but unfairly endearing. The expression caught by the camera was not Johnny's, however. Alan had never doubted that the world was his friend.

It was after the loss of this boy that Barney's and my physical relationship had faded out: not at once, but gradually. I could not have another child, and I think in his lofty mind – how contact with it made my earthier spirit infinitely earthier! – he felt that sexual association without this in view became a little sordid. I was too thoroughly smashed up to be able to do anything about combatting that idea.

Thursday came and went, with no sign of Johnny, and the following Monday, too. I gave him up, in my mind, when by Tuesday morning there had been no word at the clinic and no telephone call for me at home, either. I knew his address; it was on his attendance-form, but if he had resolved not to come there was no sense in doing what he would call 'going on' at him.

I had always been lucky in one thing: having the capacity – more, I think, than most people – of living in the present, enjoying the here and now, if anything enjoyable could be found in them. I needed this ability at that time. Under the low eave, close beside my bedroom window, a swallow's nest had hatched, the young all mouth. Morning and evening I watched the young birds being stuffed, and busied my heart with their loud satisfaction.

Each year the nest was patched and in use, and each year, throughout the rearing season, my elderly cat sat through the hours of daylight below the nest, gazing upwards steadily, whiskers quivering from time to time, while the parent-birds flickered to and fro out of reach.

Once, just once, said that patient, murderous stare, and the occasional soft sound in her throat, surely a nestling teetering on the edge of the hole before it could fly, must fall out? But this never occurred, and I took what pleasure I could from her, as well as from the young swallows clamouring so reasonably, 'Me! Me! Me!' and not bothering about anything else.

Usually I spent Wednesday morning at home. It was the time when I saw my charwoman, and made arrangements about shopping for the following week, but because of the extra private patients I had taken on, I missed her, and found a note waiting for me when I came in at lunch-time. 'Someone sounds like a foreigner didn't seem able to talk english but you cant sure' – Mrs. Harding's written messages always had a jolly breathlessness which as a rule I savoured, but this time I was desperate to know if Johnny had been the caller, and her rambling was maddening – 'rang 2 said to tell he along Thusday some time no vim so left bath.'

Thursday's appointment list was full. I sent a postcard to the violinist, asking her to bring without fail the written results of a test I had set her two sessions before, and she had been too lazy to complete. I knew she would be unwilling to tackle it at once, and would simply not appear, saying later that she had been prevented from coming by some machination of those others in the orchestra.

This made a space. Into it came Johnny with a little bunch of carnations.

'I oncie-oncied them.' He got this out successfully, before telling me that he had been in bed with influenza since we last met. He had not been able to go in for the school boxing heats after all. Under cover of curiosity about the meaning of 'oncie-oncie,' an expression I had never heard before, I was able to hide my moment of intense relief at his turning up again.

To 'oncie-oncie,' I discovered, was to go from one flower-shop or stall to another, getting away with a bloom each time. Apparently it was a well-known custom among people with relations in hospital.

Johnny laughed while he explained, watching me out of the corner of his eyes to see how I took this admission of petty shop-lifting. The police never prosecuted when a oncie-oncier was caught, knowing the Bench would dismiss the case with adverse comment: I could well imagine it 'This poor woman (man/boy) yielding to the desire for a single flower – A thing of beauty, with little intrinsic value – ' But Johnny himself never got caught, he boasted.

I looked at the carnations, all exactly the same kind and shade, with uniform length of stalk too. These had all come from the same place, at the same time. These had been bought. But to admit to buying flowers for a friend would be soft.

I accepted them casually, and we went on with breathing drills, to prevent the block establishing itself, and easing-out tricks to break it when it came.

He had made progress: he must have worked extremely hard with a mirror at home. And he had come with a list not only of ten, as I had asked, but of seventeen words which he had caught himself avoiding, or had back-tracked on, after starting to stammer. He had gone over them, talking to his reflection, with not more than three or four bad failures.

Neither his writing nor his spelling was up to the standard to be expected of a sixteen year old, and this, too, I had expected. I had intended, if I could, to change his mind about leaving school when the echoes of the battle with his father had died out in his mind, but during this session, I thought for the first time that he might be right.

Part of the recognised treatment at this stage was for the patient and the therapist to face together the grimmest aspect of the disability. To this end, I persuaded him to tell me the worst experience he could recall, connected with his stammer.

46

The incident he brought out, with mounting tension, was one in which his classmates had deliberately made a fool of him before a stranger, on a school outing to Southend. While they were in the fun-fair there, he had treated several of them to rides on the bumper cars. Being a benefactor must have meant a good deal to him. He may have given himself airs about it, which prompted their cruelty, but more likely the natural savagery of the young was responsible. On the way back to London, by train, they had hit on the idea of pretending to the ticket-collector that Johnny had all the tickets; keeping up the joke, insisting to the man that Johnny – 'that tall boy, Mister!' – had charge of the party; and he had been unable to explain he had not lost their tickets, he had never had them, only his own.

I found afterwards that, listening to this story with my hands lying in my lap, I had cut one palm with my nails. Perhaps it was as well that he should get out of the atmosphere of school.

The apparent brutality of forcing some such tale of humiliation from the sufferer worked well with Johnny: at last he gave up finally all attempts to convince me that he hardly cared if he stammered or not. Because I was personally involved, less in command of the situation than usual, I made a bad mistake soon afterwards. In this session, for the first time, the boy complained that 'they' had done nothing for him at school, meaning, about the stammer; and at home his father had done nothing either. 'Couldn't care less – ' he said, an accusation bad for his relations with Paul, complicated already by an ambivalent mixture of resentment and the need for approbation, somewhere in the family circle, to make up for his lack of prestige at school. But the complaint was a hopeful sign for the future: the boy now believed something could and should be done about what he spoke of as 'my filthy luck.'

'He has done something about it,' I said, 'so that's not quite fair, Johnny. Your father was the person who arranged for you to come here, and after all, it isn't such filthy luck you've got. Lots of people have much harder things to stand.'

Warning after warning had been given to me as a student, during my training, never to take this others-worse-than-you-line, it was always unprofitable.

Johnny reacted with anger; justified anger which made his affliction almost paralysing, and lost me nearly all the ground I had gained with him. Easy for me to talk. What did I know about it except from books? Not filthy luck, that he'd got?

'Listen. That was stupid of me – ' I broke in on his strangled efforts to convey what he wanted to say. The boy was close to tears of frustration and rage, and this particular stammerer must not cry in front of me. Soft, soft . . . I should never be forgiven. I committed deliberately a smaller sin, to get absolution for the greater one. It was unwise to be suddenly too sympathetic, encouraging self-pity, but I could not have him leave me in this state, and the bell, telling me that my next patient was here, had rung quite a long time ago. 'Of course you've had filthy luck. You still have, but it's changing. The rottenest luck. No fault of yours, it just happened to fall on you. I admit those of us who don't stammer can't really know what it's like. But you're getting to terms with the thing. Surely you know you are.'

'Skip it,' he said, rather rudely, but looked mollified.

'You must go now,' I told him. 'I've kept an old lady patient waiting, disgracefully. But I'm going to take these flowers home, and when you ring me, as I hope you will with another list of words, they'll be standing by the telephone, in a grey vase, looking wonderful.'

'Oncie-oncie you some more, one day,' he said, with not many hesitations, and my ridiculous heart sang. He would come, then, more or less regularly as the mood took him; still, he would come.

'As a favour, don't oncie-oncie for me, Johnny.'

48

'Why not? N-never caught.'

'No. Maybe. But oncie-oncied flowers wouldn't give me as much pleasure as these do,' I said, leaving him to make what he pleased of my knowing that he had come by them honestly.

*　　*　　*　　*

'I have news for you,' I said, stooping to stroke the wickering cat before going into our house. 'You're never going to catch one of those young swallows! Never!'

Still staring upwards, the cat took no notice of my hand. Not even blinking, she sat tense with longing in exactly the position in which I had left her, eight hours earlier. Barney was nearby, reading in a deck chair: his working hours started and ended before mine, on Clinic days. We had so little to talk of together that any familiar, ready-made topic, like the cat's tireless vigil, helped us through the barrenness of meeting.

He let me go past him as far as the hall before calling back, over his shoulder, 'And I have news for you!'

My mouth dried. 'What?'

'They've found a house for us, in Kowloon. That's not actually on Hong Kong island, you know, but facing it across the water, on the mainland. I'm afraid on one side it's next to some pretty down-at-heel Chinese slum property, but our place itself is quite nice, I'm told, and we're lucky to get it so soon.'

I managed to ask, not caring, whether it was furnished or unfurnished.

'Partly furnished. We bring our own crockery and linen. We can always look for somewhere else, when we're out there, if we don't like Kowloon.'

'Yes.'

'Never any difficulty about letting, in that part of the world!'

'No. If it's as overcrowded as you say.'

'You wait and see! The office is asking if we can be ready to fly out at the end of this month. They do all the booking of passages, of course, and indemnify us for what's left of our lease, here . . .' I missed several sentences, and then realised Barney was asking me what I thought we should do about the cat: was she too old to settle down in a new home, if we could find one for her?

'Oh, surely,' I said, with a passing wonder as to whether I, at thirty-two, was not the same, but the cat's alternative was not so easily available for me. 'Anyway, I wouldn't care to leave her to strangers. Will you take her down to the vet, one day soon, or shall I?'

CHAPTER V

'Leisured Persons Avoid Advance'

IN CHARACTERISTIC WAYS, everyone reacted flatteringly to the news of my departure, when I announced it at the Clinic with a set, smiling face. Of course I was sorry to leave, but how lucky I was, I conveyed, going to Hong Kong at the expense of my husband's firm. I had seen very little of the world: in fact, Brussels was as far east as I had been.

For how long should I be out of England? – Oh, there was no telling, I said. Barney was thirty-six, and would be automatically retired at sixty! Anything might happen between now and then, but the only possible step up from Hong Kong, in that particular firm, was to the New York branch.

Matron was sweetness itself about the impossibility of replacing me, except physically; but unfortunately my replacement turned out to be a young man in whom I had less than no confidence, after five minutes' conversation. This made the handing over of my patients even more painful. Having failed in his efforts to become a doctor, he appeared to despise speech-therapy, because he had managed to pass the necessary examinations.

The Almoner surpassed herself, which was a little cheering. She told me that she regretted my going so much that she would not mention something which she had been thinking of mentioning for some time, and then mentioned it. I had always been a little careless in encouraging requests for travel-vouchers. Thereby patients who lived within walking distance of the Clinic were induced to use public transport, needlessly. For elderly patients, particularly, it was hardly a good thing to be put off exercise, while they were still able to take it. Would I please impress this on my successor? We were going to overlap at work for four days only: I said I would try to remember, and immediately forgot.

The violinist took the impending change as part of the plot to prevent her from reaching her rightful position in the musical world: she had come on considerably since our straight talk but soon, I feared, would slip back into cherishing her disability. And my darling old aphasic, Mrs. Galloway, for whom I had really done very little except to be fond of her, became seriously distressed at the news, and had to be taken by taxi to her home. Here she rummaged among her meagre treasures to present me with a black lace fan, for use in the Red Sea. I have it still. I begged the young man to go on seeing her, even if he thought it a waste of time. He said in a superior way he would consider the facts of the case, which meant, I was sure, that he would not. Don was given the last of the toy horses; he would certainly have gone away with them in any case, in my distracted condition. I went on working to within three days of our flight, taking leave of friends in the evenings, and disposing by sale or gift of every-thing that was not to be sent on after us by sea.

With the two people for whom I cared most, it was as if I had already gone, from the time I told them of my going. To Clive I seemed to have said goodbye at the end of that day in the country, with the wisps of hay festooned about the hedges, and I was thankful that we need have no more protracted farewells. He was away on a medical conference abroad for my last ten days in England. I had no illusions about this love-affair, or at least few: probably no lover is without some. I had always been the one who loved the more. The whole dangerous, lovely association had been – oh, not my fault, I thought, because I saw no fault in it. But certainly, of my doing, my seeking.

Johnny sulked, from the moment he knew, and unluckily he was told not by me but by a patient in the waiting room, who saw him before I could. He burst into my room, white-faced, demanding to know if this were true, when I was just showing out Don and his mother. He behaved as if I were deserting him of my own accord, and to my despair, would not agree to go on with treatment after I left, though he had at last reached a stage when he was making truly heartening progress, visit by visit. I tried to induce him to transfer, not to my successor at the Clinic but to the man I had first recommended to his father, at another hospital – advice which was highly unorthodox, and indeed to be considered professionally unethical, but I was beyond caring. The Battersea man I considered in many ways a better technician than I was, and I said so, fighting for my son who had so strangely come back to me for help, in the guise of this ill-conditioned lad. It was my deepest need as well as his that I should get him that help. Johnny returned to saying, 'You do talk a lot of rot,' and the gagging and grimacing and back-tracking returned.

On the first possible visiting day I went to see Paul Hamilton at home, in a small house so neat and aseptically clean and polished that there was no feeling of lived-in comfort anywhere. A woman with shrewish, faded good looks was introduced as 'My housekeeper,' and justified my surmise as to why Johnny spoke a socially lower English than his father. The boy would have got little else from her, I thought: nothing in the way of warmth and unpretentious kindliness which might have gone with that accent. She was a bleak creature, over-genteel despite her voice. Paul was less aggressive in his own home, but left most of the talking to the woman.

'I'm afraid we're very disappointed with John's progress,' she said. 'I'm sure you'd rather we were quite frank?' The fact that she called him John explained why he insisted vehemently on being Johnny outside the house. 'He's been going to you for several weeks now, and I'm afraid we notice no difference.' ('I'm afraid' came from her even more often than 'Funny people about these days' from Paul). I felt a cold floor-draught of hostility flowing towards me over the glass-like surface of the linoleum.

'But there is a difference, I assure you,' I said. 'And three weeks, well, that's nothing in stammering treatment. Already he's getting the tricks of helping himself out of a tangle when he isn't nervous. This is what makes dropping the case part-way through, which I've got to do, so very unsatisfactory, and that's why I've called on you. I'm hoping you'll help if you can. If only he could be induced to go on, with this really excellent man I know – It's a question of getting him to the point where he can untie himself even when he is nervous – '

'I'm afraid we've rather given up trying to influence John. You know, of course, he's decided to leave school at once? Not even waiting till the end of the term? In order to start on that factory job!'

'No. I didn't know!' The repeated pattern in his life, of loss – or desertion as it seemed to him – at the time of his greatest need, was too strong to let Johnny behave rationally over my leaving. It was not I who was going out of his reach, but once more the woman who had been 'no good.'

'Oh, yes, if you please! He simply announced this. Mr. Hamilton said, "Well, you'd better go back to school today, and see the headmaster yourself, and collect your things." '

'Of course I could stop him legally,' Paul put in. 'Just for a few weeks. Make him finish the term. But in the mood he's in, what's the use?'

'No. I agree. No use.'

'And he's taken to using such unpleasant words in the house,' the housekeeper said primly, with some of Johnny's own irrelevancy. 'I can't think where he picked them up' – looking hard at me.

'I expect he learnt them at school, where every boy uses them,' I said, feeling that there was nothing more to lose here. 'But minor expressions like "bloody" he may be trying around the home because he's heard me say that. Believe it or not, this is a good thing to do sometimes in my job. Jolts the patient out of thinking the therapist is shut away in a separate world. Too far off to understand.'

'Fancy. Well, I'm afraid that's beyond me. Would you care for a cup of tea, or – '

'No, thank you, I'll be on my way. It was nice of you to see me.'

Despite the upheaval of his leaving school and starting work, Johnny continued to come regularly, twice a week, to make the most of the time that remained to us. The foreman seemed sympathetic, and allowed him an hour off in the afternoon, provided he made it up in the evening. We worked like beavers. Twice I took him out to tea, insisting that he should do the ordering in the restaurant. 'You'll stick, probably, talking to the waitress. Don't hope you won't. But she won't mind, you're only a customer. And you'll release yourself before I've time to say – as I shall say – "No thank you. Not cream buns for me. Too fattening. When you're my age, you'll have to start watching your waist-line".' I got no fur- ther than 'When you're – ' the first time, which pleased him, and 'for me' the second. He telephoned to me, as part of his homework, between visits.

Then Paul wrote curtly to say that the boy was stammering worse than ever and the foreman was unwilling for him to waste any more of the factory's time attending the Clinic. I got on to the foreman, a heavy but pleasant fellow. He told me he had no objection, and had never said he had. But Johnny did not appear again, nor telephone.

Our B.O.A.C. tickets arrived. We should be travelling luxuriously, first class, by one of the new Comets. ('The here and now, Clo! They've got to matter. Jets climb at an interestingly steep angle. Remember to notice. It's like playing liar-dice, Clo.')

With the tickets and labels and pamphlets of official information – all the advance cosseting of the expensive passenger – came a note from a girl I had known slightly, some years back, on holiday in Southern Ireland.

'Delighted to see from our passenger-list that you will be in my charge as far as Zurich,' she wrote. 'Thought I should warn you, in case you remember me, that I'm now an *air hostess*!' This was underlined three times, as though she considered her new position stupendous and I might have difficulty in believing the height to which she had risen. A friendly versatile creature, she had played cards with old ladies in the Connemara hotel, while it rained incessantly; and talked knowledgeably to Barney about fishing, his passion. I remembered her well, for the pleasurable scandal she caused by romping from bed to bed in the evenings, with a frigid promiscuity which she discussed with me in wide-eyed candour: 'Oh, I don't know, dear, he seemed to want it so,' was the reason given more than once for a new coupling. I was the only woman in the highly respectable establishment, a temple of trout-worship, in that most puritanical of countries, who had thought her great fun. She was good-looking in a sleek, demure style, though not really pretty, except for her notably perfect teeth.

Their white flash greeted me as I came, sick and shaken inside, up the movable steps into the aircraft. 'Hallo, Laura,' I said.

The neat head inclined slightly. 'Welcome aboard, madam, on behalf of Captain Carter, your pilot, and the crew.' There was no hint of recognition. For a second, not caring much either way, I wondered if I had accosted the wrong girl: this was the flawless, impersonal hostess. Even in uniform she looked like Laura Cairns, but B.O.A.C. specialised in flawless, impersonal hostesses, and probably had several, almost identical. 'Whoops, dearie,' breathed a voice in my ear as I passed her.

Barney was following me up the steps. He had not approved of Laura in the Irish hotel, despite her knowledge of fishing, and nodded to her curtly. 'Welcome aboard, sir, on behalf –'

In a few minutes the world as I had known and loved it would drop away, and only strangers waited ahead. The fact that it would drop away in exceptional comfort and relative splendour, so far as I was concerned, seemed singularly inappropriate, and rather an irritating absurdity.

But blessedly, at the moment of becoming airborne, Laura and I were talking as though it had been only yesterday that she bounced into our bedroom at dawn, saying, 'Would you mind pretending I've been here all night? The management's getting a bit restive. This should fox them, with the two of you!' and I had said, 'I'm damned if we will. Hop it now, like a good little trollop,' which she had taken in excellent part.

I failed to notice, after all, how fast the great plane tore up into the sky.

'How did you happen to get this job?' I asked, our lowered voices inaudible from the next chairs in the lush hum. (It was quite a roar in the Tourist Class, she informed me, lowering hers still further. But exquisitely muffled here for the lordly ones.)

'My teeth.' She was fussing over me, giving me barley sugar, tilting back my chair, showing me the gadgets.

'The skin of – ?'

'No, the colour.' She went off to attend to someone else, and then came back. 'They pick us for our teeth, you know. Much more important than the rest of us. Well, within limits. We can't be just frightful everywhere else, of course. Passengers waking up in the early morning – bit livery after the night and free drinks – What's the first thing they see? The air hostess's teeth, when we bend over them to mutter, "Would you care for a cup of tea?" They're always seeing our teeth, hard by their ear-holes: we're supposed to smile a lot. So they've got to look awfully clean, at all times.'

She leant decorously across me towards Barney, and the professional shutter came down again, temporarily. 'Could I bring you a whisky and soda, sir? Cocktail of any kind? We shall be serving lunch in about half an hour. Would you care to look at the menu beforehand?' Then to me, the shutter lifting, 'You'll wait for the champagne, won't you? Seems to me a waste to drink anything else, when it's all thrown in. But they will do it, specially men.'

She carried on with her duties, managing another little chat when she brought us lunch. 'What I was saying about teeth. Isn't it decent of Providence that whatever you do, unless it's smoking too much, it doesn't discolour your teeth?'

'I don't know that I've ever thought that one out,' I said, strangely consoled. People were kind. People were endlessly enthralling. Though I should have welcomed the plane falling into the sea, at that moment, it was not possible to be near Laura and see no gleam of human interest on the horizon.

'Oh, it's true. You can blotch your complexion and blear your eyes, but if your teeth grow good and strong, that's how they'll carry on, never mind what you do. You staying long in Hong Kong?'

'Indefinitely, Laura.'

57

'Oh, grand. I expect you'll be seeing me about every six weeks, while I'm on the Far East run. We work in relays, you understand. I'll be leaving you in Switzerland, and taking another plane on to Beirut, forty-eight hours later. I saw the address on your baggage: it isn't far from the Peninsular Hotel, where the crews hole up before we go on to Tokyo. Everyone in Kowloon runs into everyone else in Nalton Road or on the Star Ferry.'

'Good,' I said, and meant it. 'If we don't run into you by chance, come and see us.' It was about the last thing I clearly remember saying on the trip. Usually light on alcohol, I drank champagne, champagne, champagne, and needed it all. Barney grew slightly alarmed, as he told me later, and amazed, too, that the quantity I absorbed seemed to be having so little effect, outwardly.

Laura was quite right: hostesses' splendid teeth were constantly beside me. I kept from the journey a hazy recollection of smiling Indian teeth, accompanied by a gorgeous sari, between Karachi and Calcutta, and rather more clearly, for I was pulling myself together with strong coffee, of smiling Chinese teeth, to go with a becoming cheongsam, when we came down on Kai Tek runway, floating in over junks and sampans in the harbour, seventeen hours after leaving London.

The noise and scurrying, laughing, purposeful life of a Chinese street hit me as soon as the air-line transport coach turned out of the airport to take us to the town terminal. No-one had quite succeeded in preparing me for such exuberance, in spite of everything I had been told beforehand by people who had been out East. Barney at once began seeing far too many very old women, carrying far too heavy burdens on either end of a bamboo pole: it was something he remembered with distaste from his previous visit. They kept up a curious little jogging run, in time with the give of the pole. As the coach paused in dense traffic, I saw my first notice written in the two official languages, English and Cantonese, outside a shipbuilding yard. Under 'No Admittance Except On Business' were four word-characters. I pointed them out to Barney: 'That can't be a literal translation, can it! Four characters against five words. Do you know what it says?'

'Oh, it's not literal, I'm sure. It's "face." You'll have to learn about face as quickly as you can. It's you who lose face if you're curt with someone, not the person you're curt with. "No Admittance Except On Business" would be far too terse. But I don't know what the characters mean.'

A middle-aged Chinese in the seat in front swivelled round and bowed slightly, saying, 'They mean, "Leisured Persons Avoid Advance",' and he added, 'I am your servant, Missee.'

I thanked him, taking 'I am your servant' as a quaint courtesy. 'You know, Barney, I'm going to enjoy learning about face,' I said warmly, astounding myself.

He squeezed my hand, under the over-night bags we were both carrying on our knees. 'Dear Chloe. Dear, dear Chloe!' he said softly.

I think if we had been alone, if he could have kissed me then, and had kissed me, whatever he knew or suspected, life might have been different for both of us. As it was, we laughed together over the infinitely polite 'Leisured Persons.'

The man in front turned out to be really our servant, Ah Lee, who had come to the airport to meet us, in case we had heavy hand-luggage, but seeing that we had not, had refrained from disclosing who he was until we were nearly at the Peninsular Hotel, in accordance with one of those involved Chinese scruples of which I never wholly mastered the key. It had something to do with not intruding upon my meeting with the city.

Of the house itself, our first impressions were dismaying. It had an unwelcoming exterior, and the Kowloon back-street in which it stood looked poverty-stricken, and was full of flying dust from a building in full process of demolition in front. There was another a few doors away, on which breaking-up work was just starting. Inside the front door, the effect was a little better. Barney's firm had been generous to us over air-freight: all personal gear which could not easily wait for the long sea passage had been sent on ahead, and already unpacked by Ah Lee, so that some of our own possessions seemed familiar and friendly, in the large uncompromisingly square rooms. These were sparsely furnished with the sort of regulation chairs, tables, and beds to be found everywhere in Civil Service bachelor quarters, neither attractive nor displeasing. The whole air of the place was dingy, compared with the brightness and gaiety through which we had passed on the way from the airport.

'We'll get out of here as soon as we can!' Barney said. 'You'd better start looking round, Chloe, as soon as you can find your way about, alone. Sorry I shan't be able to help for a bit. Not till I've got the hang of things in the office.'

I tried hard, during my first week or two in Hong Kong, but grew first discouraged, and then beguiled from my search. There were so many things to look at idly, and so very little vacant accommodation to go purposefully to inspect. Only colossally expensive flats were available in plenty. We raised our sights, over rent, after a few interviews with uninterested agents. Still everything I looked over, which was below the new limit, turned out to be no improvement at all on what we had got. Barney found this hard to believe, but was too busy to come round and see for himself. We dared not raise the sights further. Almost his first action, on hearing that the Managership was his at last, had been to increase substantially the allowance he made to his mother, and a widowed sister: he had always been very good to them, and Barney was the last man who could go back on an offer he had made.

In England his salary had been fifteen hundred pounds a year, and my earnings varied a little above or below a thousand, according to the number of my private patients. In Hong Kong he had two thousand, as basic pay, plus a living allowance which should have been ample for us, but more than this sum was now being allocated to his family commitments. I was wholly dependent on him, a situation to which I found it hard to grow accustomed again.

I felt that I was not a good enough wife to him to complain, as if by right, about what he chose to do with his own money: he had never interfered with mine. While I had an income, I paid my share of the household bills, and could waste the rest unquestioned, if that was what I fancied. But after we reached Hong Kong I discovered, with something of a shock, that Barney the level-headed, as he had always seemed in comparison with me, had succumbed to the blandishment of an able insurance salesman, in our last disjointed days in England. He had taken on a heavy endowment policy, to safeguard his dependants if anything untoward happened to him in the Far East. Certainly his mother and sister would have been helpless without him, but as I disliked them personally as much as they disliked me, their possible plight was an unappealing reason for cutting down our standard of comfort. The premiums were out of proportion with Barney's spending-money. We were relatively hard-up in Hong Kong, and here we were expected to make something of a show, being nice to important contacts.

I suggested trying for an administrative job in one of the hospitals: though my therapy qualification was useless, experience at the Clinic might tell: no need to stress that I was a poor organizer. Barney was certain that his firm would not approve of his wife taking a small, paid job: she was required as a hostess; and the idea was dropped.

Daily I would start out to chase some rumour of a flat which would shortly be to let, reasonably cheaply, in Causeway Bay, or a tiny house in Shawky Wan, and either they were not to be found at all, or a friend of the owner had always got there first. Instead of seeking out the next, less promising address on my list, I drifted towards the typhoon shelter, to watch the life of the sampan families. This was all, from the onlooker's

61

point of view, so delightfully public: the cooking, the child-washing, the feeding of hens in coops hung out over the sterns of the boats. Delightfully public and delightfully cheerful.

I was pleased by the fire-crackers going off in the streets at any hour of the day or night, to scare away interfering evil spirits from some enterprise, just starting. As new enterprises were being launched all the time in this exciting, humming free port, the effect at times was of a continuous mild bombardment, going on in the distance.

I particularly liked the venerable Chinese guards, with beards of a few straggling grey hairs, who stood outside most of the jewellers' shops and inside all the banks, with remarkably long-barrelled rifles in their hands. Western films dealing with the bad lands in the 80's of the last century showed just such arms. Ah Lee, when consulted, assured me that not in living memory had those weapons been fired, and the oldest and frailest looking of the men were probably ex-bandits. Age being greatly respected in a Chinese community, younger, more active bandits were expected to leave alone an establishment which was supporting a worthy member of their craft.

By day, the side of me which loved the here and now, loved with thankfulness the breathtaking beauty of the harbour, set among the Seven Dragon Hills, and the junk sails like dragon wings; and at night the fantastic blaze of lights, along the Kowloon shore, and from Hong Kong itself on its island, just opposite. In loops and jewelled strings, blue, green, yellow, and red, the street-lamps and the house-lamps, and all the huge electric signs of cinemas and hotels, doubled and danced in the water which was never still.

This was a town, I found, of many circles, none of which seemed to know anything about the others. There was the Banking and International Business Circle, of which I learned through Barney's associates, when I came to know them. This centred round the various Chambers of Commerce, the Hong Kong Club (known as the Club), the Jockey Club, and the

Yacht Club – ignoring, except as a source of cheap labour, and an object for charity, the desperate lower level of humanity in the shanty-towns, spreading like sores up the hillsides; and there the squatters, in flimsy hovels clinging to land so steep that it was not wanted for development, were scarcely aware that the prosperous existed near by, save as suppliers of hard-won food. There was the University Circle, minding its own affairs outside the town: I never met any of the dons, none of the circles I knew impinged on that one at all. In the Naval Circle, the ships came and went, but H.M. dockyard remained: a pass, however, was necessary to get into it, and something of the kind, less tangible, applied to the rest of the circle. Barney having been afloat during the war, it was assumed that his wife knew how to use a knife and fork and we were occasionally admitted. The great Chinese *taipans*, said to be some of the wealthiest men on earth, were also said by everyone who met them in commercial dealings to be invariably affable, yet no-one who was not Chinese penetrated into their home life. This applied to almost all Chinese circles: the Chinese readily accepted invitations to European houses, but when they entertained in return, it would be at a restaurant, nine times out of ten. The only alien circle which it was possible for me to observe, from close-by, was the small Chinese storekeepers,' each little shop a self-contained universe. Here the shop assistants, male and female, invariably looked neat and well-found by day, but slept somehow and anyhow at night, on and under the counters, so Ah Lee said. They were fed entirely by the proprietor, as well as housed. I frequently saw them at their meals, going by relays to the dark back of the shop, when I wandered about Cat Street, looking at the curios attracting the hordes of rich tourists, another circle. Rather appetising meals, I thought by the smell; and on the first and fifteenth of the month by the Chinese calendar, they had specially good food, to celebrate the changing of the moon, I was told.

I enjoyed listening, on the ferries and in the markets, to snatches of Cantonese conversation, full of 'Ho-ho's,' which could mean 'Good,' or 'I have understood what you said,' or 'Have you understood what I said?', according to inflection. But as Cantonese was remarkably imprecise, with no tenses, so that 'I go,' 'I went,' 'Shall I go?', or 'Should I have gone?' were all covered by the same words, depending for sense on the juxtaposition with other words, like 'yesterday,' 'tomorrow,' or 'perhaps,' there was always an interesting doubt as to whether the listener had actually ho-ho'd what the speaker thought he had said. This information, too, was extracted from Ah Lee, the invaluable, not in so many words, but by long questioning. He was an admirable servant, and I spent many hours talking to him, interfering with his work by my general curiosity.

In the matter of house-hunting, after the first fortnight or so I never saw the characters for 'Leisured Persons Avoid Advance' outside any business premises without thinking, a little guiltily, that this unusually leisured person deserved less and less to advance.

Our neighbour on the left, worried looking Mrs. Kenderdine, stopped me in the street one morning to say dishearteningly that she had been trying for over six months to get away from this dirty, crowded neighbourhood, and as I could see, she had not had any success. She confided to me the rent she and her husband were prepared to pay, and it was so much higher than our ceiling that my efforts grew feebler yet. Kenderdine being a commercial traveller, they belonged to the Rotary Club Circle, which just failed to overlap with the High Executive Circle, where Mrs. Kenderdine preferred that outsiders of both should consider that she belonged by right.

'Does your husband play polo?' she asked, startling me. The idea of Barney, earnest and sedentary, careering about on a pony after a little ball, was somehow very funny. 'Because if so, I could introduce you to the riding crowd at the Club.'

'No – it's very kind of you, though – he doesn't.'

'Oh, well, I expect you both watch the cricket on Saturdays?' There was a weekly match on the pitch near the Club.

'As a matter of fact, neither of us is in the least keen on games.'

A look of dark suspicion crossed her face. 'You do play bridge?'

'No.'

'My dear, I don't know how you're going to amuse yourself in Hong Kong!'

But there was a genuine, affectionate side to her which made her pretensions tolerable: she adored Mr. Kenderdine who had to be away on his job most of the time, and whenever he was out of her care she was in a tremulous condition of anxiety lest ill should befall him.

At the end of our first month in the Colony, Barney felt that he was coming to terms with his position, and no longer needed to stay on after ordinary office hours, grappling with unaccustomed problems. He said he would help me. We might consider moving further out still: he had never minded travelling to work. There had been a brief respite from dust, when the two buildings which had been coming down at the time of our arrival were finally demolished. Now, gangs of workmen were rebuilding on both sites, and near by another dilapidated house, too rickety to be shored up any more, was about to be pulled down to make room for a day and night garage.

At the end of the second month we were still in the same place and Barney, too, was tending to find excuses for doing something else in his free hours but chase will-o'-the-wisps of accommodation. There were the floating fish restaurants, off Aberdeen, to which we were paddled out by sampan girls, and he had made several fly-fishing cronies to talk to at the Club, even if there were no river-trout in the neighbourhood. He had no use for sea-fishing.

There were moments when I was almost unbearably lonely, but for someone of my temperament Hong Kong was a better spot than most in which to be lonely. The irrepressible gaiety of the Chinese when they had nothing to be gay about was bound to be, to some extent, infective.

CHAPTER VI

Bird-watching in the New Territories

'AH LEE, WHAT'S that scratching noise?'

'Where, Master?'

I was growing accustomed to hearing Barney referred to as 'Master,' even as 'Our Master' when Ah Lee wanted to differentiate between him and some male European visitor. Then the two men were 'our Master' and 'that Master.' This evening we were alone, rather a rare occurrence in such a hospitable city: already we had a score or so of dining acquaintances. Not friends, but passers-of-time.

'Up on the roof. There!'

Ah Lee listened and announced, 'There is much wind blowing. Master heard nothing.'

But I heard the same sound two nights before, when there was no wind blowing. 'Let's go up and see, after dinner,' I said. Ah Lee was bringing in dishes, and his cooking was so good that it felt wrong to keep any meal of his waiting, although Chinese food did not spoil easily.

Ah Lee delayed us still further, when the coffee had been served, by insisting that Missee must have her dark glasses, before she went out, and as usual she had mislaid them. Earlier in the day a speck of grit had lodged in my eye, and it had taken the combined efforts of Ah Lee and wash-amah to get it out. I could not see that sun-glasses, open at the sides, would be any real protection from the eddies of dust swirling about the roof, but it seemed churlish to protest, after the trouble I had given. We sat on, while he rummaged about the house: he was much more skilful than I was in finding lost things.

The small accident had been my own fault. I was still fresh enough from England to stand and stare, fascinated, at workmen running on a job. On the opposite side of the road, where the old building had been pulled down at startling speed, the new one was going up nearly as fast, gangs toiling all night, by kerosene flares, in relays. The air was thick with powdered cement. I had gazed, wide-eyed, too long, asking for trouble.

Ah Lee found my glasses. There was nothing on the roof when we reached it, through a trap door at the top of a fire-escape ladder. Nothing but blowing dust, and a little rubbish which might have come with the dust, or been thrown over from the next roof. Ours was flat, and continuous with those of the buildings on either side of us. Like the Kenderdines', on our left, our roof was surrounded by intricate festoons of barbed wire, in a barrier about six feet high, to prevent encroachment from anywhere, but particularly from the Chinese tenement on our other side, where a family of roof-squatters had long been established. Barney, who always knew statistics, told me that upwards of eighty thousand people were believed to be living, that summer, on the roofs of Kowloon and Hong Kong. The numbers went up a little whenever some ramshackle doss-heap was smashed up by its owners, in order that something more profitable should rise in its place.

These were the nomad family groups, about ninety per cent of them recent refugees from across the Red border, who could find no niche in the shanty-towns, nor in the jammed tenements, and the Government had not yet been able to rehouse them in the giant settlement-blocks going up wherever space could be cleared for them.

Pitiable or not, they were also the people whom every respectable property owner hoped to keep off his own roof, hence the wire. Without water, without sanitation, without means of support other than the official charity hand-out of a little rice and salt fish, they were a menace in every way to the householder below.

'You'd better have a good look round our wire, Ah Lee, in daylight tomorrow!' Barney said as we went down again, and Ah Lee agreed. Master was always right, I was the one he bullied. He had realised at once that Barney was a perfectionist, and I was anything but: he remained tender, however, towards my 'face.' He informed Barney that I had made an excellent bargain with the wash-amah, engaging her to work for us two days a week, when in fact he had taken on the girl, whom he called his niece, without consulting me at all, at a sum which I should have been ashamed to offer her.

He never refused to let me do the daily shopping, in the great markets which I liked visiting: the mounds of strange-coloured tropical fish were a glory to the eye. I longed for some regular duties to fill my day, apart from abortive house-hunting. More than once I told him firmly that the next morning I definitely wished him to take me along when he went to the market, and show me which were the stalls for the freshest fish, meat and vegetables, and how much I ought to pay. He gave me his deferential bow, said, 'Yes, Missee,' and later slipped away while I was on the telephone, or in the bathroom. The excuse was either that Master had wanted something in a hurry, or if he had not gone at that moment, lunch could hardly have been ready, for me and my friends, at the time I had asked. Ah Lee would have lost face if I had been forced to keep guests waiting. He was never late. Once, by standing ready in the hall till he felt there was no escape, I got my way, but the next day, when I said I would go again, he maintained that we were stocked up with perishables for a week, and proved it by not going down to the market himself. By dealing only with his friends and relations, we probably paid no more squeeze than I should certainly have been forced to pay if I went alone. He won; I never managed to do the shopping regularly. All I bought were personal things, like flowers for dinner parties, and small luxuries.

Two nights after we had gone up to the roof, I heard the scrabbling noise again, but was unable to investigate. I was being hostess to a group of lunatic, amiable naval bird-watchers, who had come into the harbour that morning in the *Emerald* and the *Calliope*, destroyers of the Far Eastern fleet.

It was our first really big dinner party under Ah Lee's eye, and not under his eye alone. Several Chinese servants who had already handed me cocktails in other people's houses, had been called in, like the wash-amah, on his own initiative; they brought with them some nice Georgian silver, which disappeared again when they left. As we were never asked to pay for these extra waiters, who materialised from time to time in our house, perfectly dressed in starched white uniforms, and as Ah Lee himself occasionally disappeared in the evening, after finding out that we were not expecting anyone, I assumed it was a reciprocal arrangement. His prestige would suffer if our prestige suffered, through our hospitality not being good enough.

He had taken great trouble with the dinner, for which there had been very little notice, deciding the menu himself, and producing four perfect courses. Missee had been thanked for her offer of help in the kitchen for the occasion, but practically shooed out of the way.

Presiding over the coffee tray – not ours, but much better – I had not the nerve to desert my post to go up to the roof because of a sound which might be no more than the scampering of a rat or something loose, caught in the wire, tapping in the wind.

The meal was capped by excellent brandy and cigars, which Master had told him to buy, according to Ah Lee the next morning, but Barney had in fact forgotten, in the pleasure of meeting again a wartime shipmate.

This man was now Commander Lory: he and Barney had been something much lowlier together at Scapa. Claiming that his spies had informed him of Barney's unheralded arrival in Hong Kong and present address, ten minutes after the *Calliope* berthed, he had appeared on our doorstep at breakfast time, to invite us both to a bird-watching expedition to the New Territories the next day. Saying no to the expedition, Barney had counter-invited him to dinner. He brought with him in the evening, to help persuade us to come, seven members of the Royal Naval Bird-Watching Society, Far East Section, yet another circle which, I gathered, had as little to do as possible with any other circle based on Hong Kong, including the rest of the naval detachment in these waters. They were single-minded enthusiasts to a man, and I was always easily charmed by any monomaniac's assumption that sane persons must share his obsession.

Before our guests arrived Barney had warned me, 'Don't be stampeded into agreeing to go. You're so weak with people. I've told you what I went through!'

During his first visit to Hong Kong he had been inveigled out on the same sort of expedition, though not then with Lory. The object was to list the species of autumn migrants flying southwards over the Red Chinese border. What happened was that he had spent the day leaping wildly from bund to bund in pursuit of more agile companions in the far distance, who thought they had seen a scorfe-duck come by, landing safely in British territory, and wanted to verify this. The bunds, narrow mud paths raised a foot or so above the level of the flooded paddy-fields, were extremely slippery. Once was enough. Nothing would induce Barney to face a similar ordeal, fifteen years older and considerably heavier, even though the next day happened to be Sunday and he would have been free to go. And I should have the sense to learn from his experience.

'Don't understand what's happened to your Old Man, Mrs. Freeborn!' Lory mourned. 'He used to watch birds with me in Scapa all the time.'

I saw Ah Lee glance irritably at the ceiling. Noticing that I had observed this, he lowered his eyes and busied himself with the guests. Rats might come across from the gruesomely dirty looking tenement next door, but would rats scamper and then keep still for quite a long while, and afterwards make a slow, gentle, dragging sound?

'In Scapa,' I said, 'unless I'm mistaken, there was nothing else to watch and no opportunities for fly-fishing.'

'Ah, well, you've got something there.'

I was giving the Commander such poorly divided attention that it left him altogether at times. If there were people living on our roof, how had they got there, without obviously disturbing the barrier wire, and how did they remove all traces so quickly, when necessary?

'You just have to accept,' I said, 'that my husband was never really keen on things with feathers.'

'But you'll come, won't you, Mrs. Freeborn? We want to try a specimen count, over five miles, along the border, and we could do with at least two more counters.'

Suddenly I remembered that an excellent tart, which we had only just started the previous day, had unaccountably disappeared when I asked for it again, for lunch. At the time I had thought nothing of this. Ah Lee was entitled to eat whatever he wanted; and so was the wash-amah, on her days with us; but it had been a large and very succulent dish, and it had not been one of wash-amah's days. When I came round, as it were, I found it was being taken for granted that I was coming on the count. 'You've no idea how lucky we are,' Lory was saying. 'Slap on the migration line from Japan, and we get the south-eastern stream from inland, too. They converge here. Of course it's every bird-watcher's favourite station. Waders, eagles, harriers: they all ought to be on the

71

move tomorrow. Got powerful binoculars? Not that it matters, because we can lend them.'

'Look here, I don't want to see the inside of a Communist gaol,' I protested.

'Rather not. Why should you?'

'Because if you and your friends are going to lie spread out at intervals along five miles of the frontier, gazing through powerful glasses into Red China, do you really think people on the other side will believe you're counting harriers? Your information service must be pretty good, the way you knew at once where to find Barney –'

'It's not bad,' he said complacently.

'Well, if half the things I'm told about this town are true, their spy system is pretty good, too. So of course they'll know you're the Navy, even if you are in plain clothes. I just don't want to be hauled across that frontier.'

'Not to worry,' he said, looking at me as fondly as if I had been a meadow-pipit. 'Ours is pretty good, as you say, but theirs is much better. So much better, they'll know we're the Navy, all right, but they'll also know, don't you see, that we're genuine bird-watchers. The Royal Naval Bird-Watching Society's been going for years.'

'Oh, they'll know all that, will they? You're sure of that?'

'Quite. We're often around up there, in the New Territories, at the migration time. When the ship's in port, that is, naturally. But it's surprising how often she is. *Emerald*, too. Captain's a member of the Society. Very keen. All you'll have to do tomorrow, about the frontier, is to wave occasionally to the little spy they'll put on to watch us – they always do. Wave at him any time you see him fiddling with his binoculars. So they know we know who he is. We think it's good for morale. If you can get yourself to the Dockyard by seven in the morning – the Star Ferry starts running at five, you know – we'll take you over to Stonecutter's Island for breakfast, and then on from there. Don't be late, will you? We ought to get stonechat, and Daurian restart – Now there's a really lovely little bird for you. I don't suppose you've seen one yet? Whimbrel and curlew. It should be a first class day.'

Whatever Barney said of its possible horrors, I was rather pleased to be going on the expedition. It would fill up a day. I did not want time on my hands, especially at weekends, and interesting and varied and beautiful as the town was, I had by then had just about enough of walking around Hong Kong by myself.

'I think you're being very unwise,' Barney told me when the guests had gone. 'You don't know what you're letting yourself in for.' As usual, he was right. 'And what about that flat you were going to look at tomorrow, in Magazine Gap?'

'Gone,' I said, absolving myself, or almost, by the thought that this was probably true. Indeed, practically for certain. Anything relatively inexpensive in Magazine Gap was sure to be taken swiftly. Arguments with Barney tended to go on and on, unless I gave in; he had so much more stamina. In a minute, if I let him, he would start suggesting that there was still time to ring up *Calliope* by shore-line and tell Lory that I had changed my mind.

I wanted the chance to go up to the roof alone. I could hear Ah Lee still washing up in the kitchen: our phantom staff had melted away, along with the borrowed Georgian silver. I suggested that Barney should go in and say formally, on behalf of us both, how much we appreciated the efforts which had been made over the dinner. Ah Lee would be far more gratified by a man's praise.

Again I found the roof bare of any kind of life, when I put my head out of the trap-door. By the light of the street-lamp below, and the flares on the scaffolding opposite, I could see nothing wrong with the wire, in a quick glance round. On the neighbouring roof, beyond the barrier, the squatters were asleep in their dreadful huddle of shelters, made of broken wood, sacking, and petrol cans beaten flat. Or perhaps they

73

were not asleep but merely unable to afford any light in the hovels. A diffused glow came from the blaze of illumination in the town, as well as from the other lights, enough for me to notice a few marks on the roof on our side of the wire which I had not seen before, I thought. Rats had not made those scratches. Standing on the steep fire-escape stairs, I let the trap down very gently, rebolting the heavy fastenings on the inner side by touch alone – we had no light on the top landing, which had on it only the wash room and a big attic for trunks and boxes. Once the door was shut again it was very dark.

Barney and Ah Lee were still talking in the kitchen: they must have gone over the wonderfully improvised meal course by course. I could hear the murmur of voices, but not the words until I reached my bedroom, and then Ah Lee said deferentially, 'If Master is pleased, I am pleased.' Master would look at the bills even less carefully when he paid them on Saturday mornings. They were never itemised, in any case, but were put before him in the form of 'From the fish-stall – so much. From the meat-stall – so much.' Barney thought Ah Lee a splendid fellow: so did I : but I fancied we thought it in slightly different ways.

I was in bed and ostensibly asleep before Barney came up, to avoid further argument, and then, some time after his breathing had told me that he was really asleep, I started worrying, in the desultory way which allows sleep to come for a few minutes, and suddenly banishes it: had I shot those bolts properly, fumbling in the darkness? Whatever was using our roof I wished to stay on our roof and not penetrate further, at least until I knew what it was. I took Barney's torch without disturbing him, and climbed the stairs again. The bolts were all right. Something small and pale lay on the wide top stair, where it might or might not have been an hour or so before, when I came without light. Examined in the beam of the torch, it turned out to be a fragment of pastry stained dark on one side. We had eaten rice-bird pie. The fire-escape stairs were extremely narrow: this was the natural place where anyone would rest a dish, in order to have hands free for the bolts.

I was fairly sure that I could hear slight movements outside. Something alive was there, but alone and at this time of night, I was not going to look. If we were feeding the roof-squatters from next door I did not mind particularly, but it was hard to think of a reason for Ah Lee to risk his job in this way. These people could not possibly be bribing him adequately: if they had any money at all they would not be roof-squatting. Indiscriminate charity was not, by tradition, a Chinese characteristic. But curiosity could be satisfied at too high a price, I decided. I would think several times before investigating further. Barney would certainly put a stop to whatever was going on. Ah Lee was being mildly dishonest, but there was no such thing as mild dishonesty so far as Barney was concerned: people were honest, or they were not. And face might require Ah Lee to leave us if he was proved to have been lying: he had committed himself by saying that Master heard nothing on the roof.

This place without Ah Lee's ministrations was unthinkable: I had become quickly accustomed to the fibre-softening luxury of dropping garments on the floor with the certainty that they would be picked up, pressed or washed or mended as necessary, and folded neatly back among my other things, before I thought of wanting them again.

I crept back to bed, and to sleep, and had great difficulty in rousing myself in the morning, in time to get to the Dockyard by seven. Ah Lee, however, was there to see – indeed, to insist – that Missee had a cup of tea before starting. He had refused to live in, though we had room enough, and we never learned where he slept: whenever he was asked a question which he preferred not to answer, he replied volubly to some other, unasked question instead. Neither Barney nor I ever got up early without finding him in the kitchen, presiding over our primitive charcoal stove.

My day of bird-watching in the New Territories turned out to be very pleasant, and luckily less strenuous than Barney predicted. With the Navy as my hosts, I had the lightest-hearted few hours which had come my way since the news of the move from England was broken to me: the day in the country with Clive had been blissful, but scarcely light-hearted.

The only depressing element in the excursion, and typical of Hong Kong's odd strategic position, was the behaviour of the little Communist spy who was waiting near his side of the frontier when we approached ours. He kept us under observation from about half a mile away, and though we waved to him genially, across that grim border, whenever, through our binoculars, we caught him refocussing upon us, he never once waved back.

Very strange, to me, was the feeling that came from looking across at the unreachable, scruffy villages on the Chinese side, which appeared so very much like the scruffy, British-side villages through which we had just passed, on our way up through the New Territories.

Lying on the mainland, between Kowloon and the Red border, these New Territories must by treaty be handed back to China within forty years: intensive cultivation but few long-term projects for developments were going on there. I could see how satisfactory this was to the bird-watchers, if not to the local inhabitants. There were birds everywhere, but they were thickest of all in the undisturbed borderland.

Resting on our stomachs, propped up on our elbows, we had the autumn sun on our backs, and this seemed to me an excellent way of watching anything, after heavy-going by paddy and bund on the last lap of the journey up to the frontier: the Navy's jeeps were left about a mile away. Even if the bund-leaping had not been as athletic for me on this trip as for Barney on his, I welcomed a breather. Lory had thoughtfully brought along, for my protection, a sampan girl's hat, left aboard *Calliope* by one of the families which always painted the vessel when she came into Hong Kong. Under it I could half doze, while next to me the *Emerald's* commanding officer, either a splendid liar or endowed with miraculous vision, identified dot after dot in the sky which I could barely see, with long sight slightly above normal. As all but one of the rest of the party were his officers, or those from a sister-ship, no-one questioned his statements that coming over at two o'clock was a female pied harrier with a godwit, no, two godwits, and a red-backed shrike, by Jove, between ten and eleven. These migrants were written down in the Society's log, temporarily kept by the other civilian, Tom Jarvis, who, like me, had been more or less press-ganged to make another counter. He was a constructional engineer, working for the time being on Kai Tek airfield, where the runway was to be extended.

I distinguished myself by confusing rollers with godwits, and both with bulbuls (bulbuls were no good, for some reason, and ought not to be reported), even after the birds had been identified for me several times: but everyone was very nice about it. I was relieved to notice that Jarvis was nearly as incompetent, which was why he had been relegated to log-keeping.

Catching my eye, he gave me a fleeting grin, while entering some particularly confident claim by the *Emerald's* commander, whose eyes were busy with his binoculars.

Aware that we were technical outcasts, only tolerated by the invincible good manners of the Navy, we walked together at the start of the journey home, and talked instead of keeping a bright look-out. The party straggled out: we were taking a roundabout way down from the hills along the frontier, to include some coverts and marshy patches where early visitors had been reported in other autumns. It was on this part of the expedition that I first saw the girl I was to know later as Honuong.

A thin, dirty little figure of indeterminate age, in the usual coolie uniform of blue cotton jacket and trousers, she was cutting wood by the side of the footpath, which wound, here, through timbered country, about a mile and a half from the frontier. Tom Jarvis called something to her in Cantonese, to which she replied with a smile, showing two rows of unusually pointed teeth. They were like a fox's, and showed up more brilliantly because of the grime on her face. Their cleanness, though not their shape, made me think of Laura's one perfection. She gave herself a brief rest, leaning against the considerable pile of chopped wood.

'What did you say that pleased her so much?' I asked.

'It was just a greeting. Using up almost all the Cantonese I can command, I told her, "You have eaten your morning rice and are cutting wood".'

'Why should that go so well? She doesn't look as if she's had any rice for a long time. Or not much of it, anyway. And she must know she's cutting wood.'

'All I know I've picked up from our workmen on the job. It's polite, by Chinese standards, to tell people they've had rice, and what they're doing. The foreman of one of the gangs making wooden moulds for a special kind of cement post happens to be a very interesting old man. We talk quite a bit in a mixture of languages. He gave me the Cantonese for cutting wood.'

'It sounds absurd, telling people what they're doing.'

'No more absurd than saying, "How do you do?" in reply to "How do you do?", which you and I did, a little while back.' Jarvis had a nice smile.

'No, come to think of it, I suppose not!'

The Chinese girl returned to her wood-chopping, going hard at it, after a pause of less than a minute, wielding a heavy axe with matchstick arms.

78

'How they work!' Jarvis said as we walked on. 'I'll never see a Chinese face in England, when I've finished my stretch out here, without wondering how long I shall be allowed to live on there, in a relatively drone-like way. Where one comes, more are coming. And with their energy, and their guile, and their good temper, they're bound to inherit the earth, eventually.'

'Look, isn't that a bunch of waders of some kind?' I said conscientiously. 'Oughtn't we to be counting them?'

'Oh, not now we're off the frontier, surely? Let's not bother. Till the Chinese do conquer the earth, there's some compensation for not being such self-sweaters as they are, don't you think? It makes life much pleasanter, and easier.'

'All right, we didn't see those birds,' I agreed. 'I daresay they weren't waders after all,' and I turned my eyes from bushes on one side of the path ahead of us. An old crone with a bamboo carrying-pole had just passed, going in the opposite direction, tottering under the weight of two small haystacks, and wisps of her load had caught in the thorns, hanging there waiting for me to go by. Hong Kong in autumn had borrowed the brief glory of an English summer: this was a green and gold day. It was unfair of the world to be so much alike, in far-separated places.

I talked quickly to Jarvis of anything which came into my mind, asking questions about labour conditions, describing the way buildings avalanched down and rushed up in our road in Kowloon. I would hold my thoughts on the here and now. 'How can men keep up such a pace, night and day?' I said. 'When on the whole they're such a scrawny looking lot?' Soon we should have gone by.

'Well, if you really want to know how they manage, it's like this –'

Tom Jarvis would never guess how grateful I was to him for talking on steadily, without much prompting, when the ache for time out of reach came upon me, like a black beast hiding in my mind, waiting to pounce as soon as my guard was weakened by trivial, unexpected things: hay caught in a bush.

'Yes, I'd like to understand. I'm not a bird-watcher any more than you are. I'm a person-watcher. And so are you, I think?'

'Certainly, a person-watcher! The key is that no Chinese workman accepts a job on his own. I learnt that my first week out here. A coolie hears a rumour that something's going to be demolished or built. He goes to the contractor and says, "My three brothers and I, and my second brother's four brothers-in-law, with their five uncles, will do this work for you in three weeks from now, for so much in cash." Then they begin to run, as you've noticed. They always finish by the time agreed, but if they do better than that, they can get going sooner on another job, and make more money, quicker, as a family gang. A fair number of them take opium, to help them through a spate of work without rest.'

'I thought opium gave you beautiful daydreams and then sent you to sleep?' I objected. We had passed the hay wisps, the path was in open ground, approaching a village. I could look about again. Towards my companion I felt warmly, and really wanted to hear what he was saying.

'Well, the stuff's got two effects. Some of our Chinese – that foreman for one – will use it both ways at different times. Smoke enough for pleasure and you can't work. Smoke less, and you can borrow strength from tomorrow.'

'Though you have to pay back sometime in complete exhaustion?'

'Yes, but what he says is, if you can arrange your going-to-pieces period to come between jobs, when one of the gang is finding out which of two future projects will pay better, why not? You see what I mean about inheriting the earth?' He broke off with, 'Mind where you're walking! I suppose this must be where the wood-cutting girl lives, poor little devil!'

We were among hovels, and within their smell. The path had turned into the main drain of the village. If the country-side, between the clusters of dwellings, looked like unspoilt Hampshire to a troubling extent, this collection of huts was unmistakeably Far Eastern. In the city of Hong Kong and Kowloon combined, fantastic overcrowding went with the hope of work, at any rate: in the New Territories, from what I could see, there was plenty of free space, away from the market gardens established along the main roads, but almost complete destitution and practically no chance of employment at all. This was a particularly noisome spot.

Pigs were rootling about in the filth, unfamiliar-looking oriental pigs, longer and lower in the body than any I had seen elsewhere, and with turned-up snouts. Several chow dogs were among them, but the pigs were the lords, the dogs gave them right of way, warily. Another tough old crone, her face a deep brown map of intersecting wrinkles, manoeuvred her enormous loads past us with difficulty. My companion informed her she was carrying much stone, and her dignified wrinkles split up into a glittering display of gold teeth. Her hands free, with all the weight on the pole across her bent shoulders, she patted my arm and tried to tell me something. She was not begging, nobody begged from us that day in any of the dreadful villages, but she urgently wanted to make her-self understood. Tom Jarvis's Cantonese, however, was not equal to this, and presently she ran on, her bare feet slapping into the slime.

I was glad Barney was not there. He would have been so angry with mankind in general – rightly, of course – for letting her live like this, that he could not have approved of her personally for being so enduring. I could not help approving.

Wealthy though it was, the small colony of Hong Kong had accepted an immense burden in trying to assimilate the unending flow of refugees out of China: pockets of horror were inevitable, or so it seemed to me: but no-one would ever prevail on Barney to accept that view.

Commander Lory caught up with Jarvis and me. 'Spotted anything interesting?' We shook our heads. 'Rather fancy I saw a Drake's kingfisher back in that marshy bit. Unconfirmed, though,' he said modestly. 'Unfortunately none of the others got it. You're sure you didn't? Pity – Does one good, doesn't it, to see these old girls smile? Never mind what they're toting, they smile.'

'It doesn't so much do me good,' I said. 'It staggers me! What have they got to smile about?'

' "What have they got – ?" ' Some of the smile came off his own face. He looked taken aback. 'My dear girl, they have plenty to smile about, and what's more, they know it. They wouldn't thank you for sympathy! It isn't as if they were living the other side of the frontier, where, as you must have noticed, everything looks pretty grim.'

Tom Jarvis observed mildly, 'Everything looks pretty grim just here, to me.'

I said, 'Commander Lory, you tell me what they've got to smile about, these people in this village? Suppose you were eighty, or nearly, and ghastly poor, and still working as few people would dare work an animal at home, in revolting conditions, what would you be smiling about?'

Without sharing Barney's social conscience, I could not share, either, Lory's happy feeling that everything was all right because old ladies could smile. Barney's ex-shipmate was a kind, friendly obsessive, but unluckily, at the moment, he reminded me by that ' – wouldn't thank you' of the Almoner at the Clinic, who was obsessive without being friendly or kind. After the nice sandwiches and the welcome beer, and the good company with which he had provided me, on this entertaining expedition, I felt, looking back, that I had inexcusably bitten the hand that fed me. But Lory was not easily ruffled. He came back superbly with, 'British rule, that's what they've got. And don't they appreciate it! Now when we get to that scrub ahead, it's worth keeping your eyes skinned for broad-billed rollers, and we might flush a purple heron from those reeds.' He hurried on.

'Do you really think it matters to anyone, old and hungry and without any money, who holds the reins – ' – but he had gone, out of conversational range unless I shouted.

Much later, it came round to me that he remarked in the Yacht Club, 'Poor old Freeborn! Afraid he's got hitched up with a rather Bolshi type. Nice woman, personally, mind you. Had her out bird-watching and she got really interested.' And then he added the kiss of death: 'Clever, I believe. Does something professionally. But I don't know what.'

Tom Jarvis and I exchanged glances again, and laughed. 'Of such is the kingdom of Hong Kong,' he said irreverently. 'I've been here about as long as you have, I gather, and I've discovered that among all the other things this place is, it's the last stronghold of the Blimps, since Cyprus turned dirty on them, and Africa isn't what it was.'

'If they don't stray far from the Club, or the Peak, or the racecourse,' I suggested, 'they can avoid meeting any but their own kind, hereabouts?'

'That's right. But Lory is the very decentest sort. He meets the others, but he hardly ever listens to what they say, so it comes to the same thing. Do you understand the reason for the gold he was talking about, in the poor old ladies' mouths?'

'No.' More and more I felt at ease with someone interested in everything going on around him. Tom Jarvis was tall and lanky, not specially handsome, but alive in a pleasantly diffused way. For me, the first attraction was that he was fundamentally gay. Without realising it then, I was very hungry for intelligent gaiety.

'Well, that gold doesn't mean that the teeth ever needed mending. They may have done, of course, but not necessarily. What it does prove, in a woman over about fifty, is

83

that she was something of a looker in her youth. A nice-mannered Chinese lover gives a gold tooth-cap as a farewell present. Or did, when he could afford to. Manners are changing. If he wasn't intending to marry the woman himself, he accepted, and so did she when they parted, that one day she would be utterly devoted to her children by another man. To her whole family. The family is everything to the Chinese.'

'Yes, I do know that,' I said.

'It's the one thing you can always be sure of, family loyalty. Not to the small family unit, but the whole ramification of aunts and grandparents and cousins. It's bound to become the woman's dearest ambition to pass on whatever she can to her family, when she dies. Best of all, to her children. If the man gives money when he leaves her, it may get stolen or spent. Besides, money has a way of sticking to lawyers' fingers, in any inheritance. But there's no loss and no trouble at all in inheriting gold capped teeth. All her children may need is a hammer. You see?'

'This is gruesome but fascinating,' I said. I was suddenly resolved to see much more of the life of the people around me, living on such widely spaced levels. I would have a look at the conditions in the tenement next door, as soon as possible.

I came back from this excursion in the late afternoon to find Mrs. Kenderdine, from the house on our left, in tears in our sitting room. Barney was doing his best to cheer her with sherry, but as this appeal to us for comfort was the second of its kind within quite a short period, neighbourly duty rather than concern showed in his manner. Mr. Kenderdine was away on his job, collecting patent medicine orders in the Philippines, and his wife was worried by not hearing from him.

To be apart was, for this pair, childless and elderly, to be naked to all the winds of anxiety that blew. Each believed that the other had a weak heart, though whether or not there was

84

any truth in this idea, we could not tell: they both looked healthy enough. It was only after he had been gone for some days that Mrs. Kenderdine tended to appear on our doorstep, saying, 'I can't bear it alone any longer –'

If he were in Yokohama or Singapore, and a riot, earthquake or epidemic happened to be reported anywhere in Japan or Malaya, he was inclined to assume that Mrs. Kenderdine was bound to hear of it, by radio or newspaper, and jump to the conclusion that he must be in the midst of whatever it was, so he would send her a telegram telling her not to worry: the most alarming thing he could do. This, at any rate, was the pattern of the trouble, the first time she came round to cry with us. On the second occasion she was so incoherent, we were never sure what had gone wrong in the Philippines.

So far as we could make out, Mrs. Kenderdine – not having seen any report of trouble in Manilla, and receiving the wire that he was all right – immediately felt convinced that he was in danger of some kind, and replied begging him to get in touch with her by long-distance telephone as quickly as possible. This was where vagueness set in. Either he did not want to spend the money, which was heartless of him when he knew how she felt about his cardiac trouble. Or, more probably, because he was moving about rapidly, he had left the place to which her message was addressed before it could reach him.

If so, Barney and I felt, this was just as well, for he would undoubtedly have been overwhelmed by the fear that her heart was bothering her again. As it was, he had neither telephoned, nor telegraphed a second time. We came down heavily in support of the explanation that he had not received her communication, but for a long while Mrs. Kenderdine could not accept this. These two people were rapidly reassuring one another towards nervous breakdowns, but no-one could help liking them in their absurdity. She perked up after a while, and before she left, was wondering if she should let him know, in due course, the cheerful issue of the typhoon menace, which had been much in public conversation in the last few days. Appalling typhoons had struck the island in the past, and would again. This one had only threatened to flick us with its tail, in passing, but changing course, had safely and harmlessly swept out into the China sea. No, we said. Better not mention it. These winds had been known to circle.

'I think,' Barney said when she had left us, 'tea only, next time. Not sherry. This dependence on us and alcohol combined could easily become a habit. After all, as a commercial traveller, Kenderdine's bound to be away three months out of four.' For once we were in complete accord.

I called Ah Lee and asked if he could arrange for me to see over the tenement next door, or at least over some part of it.

'Why Missee want that? Not a good place. Too dirty. She will come back fleas all over.'

'Then I'll go into the bathroom as soon as I get back, drop all my clothes on the floor, have a bath, put everything I've worn into the bathwater, to drown the fleas, and get into clean things. I want to see how families live there. How much floor-space they have. How they sleep and cook – that sort of thing.'

Ah Lee remained obstructive. Not suitable.

'And there's another thing I'd like,' I said. 'In future, I want to do the household shopping myself. I know you do it very well indeed – probably better than I shall – but I want to learn how. You remember I've mentioned this before? And the only way to learn is to try it. I'm not used to doing nothing. You take me down to the Central Market tomorrow, at nine o'clock, and show me where we buy, and how much we pay.' If we were feeding others besides ourselves, this would be the last thing he would wish to do.

He bowed, and gave way a little over the tenement. He would approach, he said, a family he happened to know slightly. They had part of one floor, and they could show me how they managed, which was much how everyone else got along.

That would do nicely, I told him. Would he please contact these friends of his as soon as possible?

Nevertheless, I still meant what I said about the shopping, and repeated the demand on several other occasions, until somehow, in view of all my previous defeats, it became too embarrassing to go on asking, the embarrassment being all on my side. Ah Lee remained imperturbable, and master of the situation. The formula with which he presented the bills to Master never varied: 'Missee wish me to buy – ' When Barney complimented his staff at the office on finding us such a well-trained houseman, to offset the poorness of the accommodation, the colleague who was always apologising for not having done better, over the house, denied all knowledge of Ah Lee. A woman had been engaged for us. We never saw her: possibly Ah Lee had bought her off before we arrived. Either he went with the premises, owned by the Chinese landlord of the tenement next door, or he had appointed himself to the job.

My only victory over him, in the first few months of our association, was the visit to our neighbours on the right. I returned stubbornly to the subject the next morning.

'Have you spoken to the people you know in the tenement?'

Unfortunately, he said, they had moved away. But he offered to produce the proprietor 'this day week.' And the proprietor would be happy to make any arrangement Missee cared to ask.

'No, I don't want to see the proprietor. He'd only tell me a lot of lies about charging nothing more than Government-controlled prices. While his tenants know, if they tell anyone what they're really paying – well, anyone who might be an inspector, or know an inspector – out they go, at once. That would have been made clear to them, wouldn't it, when they

87

hired sleeping-space from him? And they're afraid of not being able to find anywhere else to go.'

'Missee learn fast! Such a short time in Hong Kong.' This was the first occasion on which I saw Ah Lee smile. 'But that proprietor, he is my third uncle's cousin. A good man.'

'Oh, I'm sure. But I still don't want to see him.'

'The house is dirty because the people in the house are dirty people. How can he help that?'

'I don't know. I don't suppose he can. All I want is to talk to some of the tenants. Have a look round.'

'By the way,' interrupted Barney, who had just come down to breakfast, 'were there noises on the roof last night? I slept very soundly. Shouldn't have heard anything if there was anything to hear.'

'I don't think there was,' I said, and did not pursue this subject. (For several nights to come, there was not a sound; and dishes which had appeared on our table in one form, returned in another: we were eating our left-overs ourselves.)

About the visit to the tenement – Ah Lee went on objecting. 'Most people on floors have no English. Missee has not yet quite enough Cantonese.' (I had none, as he knew, beyond 'Ho-ho.')

'Then tell the wash-amah to come with me. She knows a little English.'

'She would not like to go in there. Too dirty. Get fleas.'

'Isn't she your niece?' We looked one another in the eye. He accepted that no-one, however stupid, or white, could live in the lower parts of Kowloon for any time at all without realising that the authority of a man was complete over the younger women, in all Chinese families. 'And when she comes back with me,' I said, 'she can have Master's bathroom, drop her clothes, wash, drown the fleas, put on clean things, same as me.'

'Oh, no!' He was scandalised. In Master's bathroom? Her fleas could wait. We went the next morning.

Barney continued to say, at intervals, that he meant to take up social work as soon as the stress of the new job allowed, but he seemed in no hurry to meet the kind of people he might be going to help. Asked if he would like me to put off the visit till the evening when he could come with me, he thought the idea even less attractive than the expedition to the New Territories: 'I don't feel extreme poverty should be treated as a show, Chloe. All right if you were going for a purpose. Not just from curiosity.'

CHAPTER VII

'Cumshaw!' 'Cumshaw!'

AN OLD MAN on a shelf half-way up one wall, on the ground floor of the tenement, slept with his knees drawn up, in order that a grandson, about nine, crouching in the space saved in this way, could make a plastic flower to sell. The boy had just finished one, neatly, and was starting on a second, when I came by.

These were people the wash-amah knew. At the time, plastic flowers were one of Hong Kong's great exports, and most of them were made by piece-work. With the proceeds from several flowers, the wash-amah explained, the family hoped to buy the materials to make a reed mat. I wondered if it had been the old man himself who had discovered that by getting accustomed to this painfully cramped position, he could help the family income, or if the others had discovered this for him.

Wash-amah's English was not equal to dealing with ideas, only with a few facts. I learnt that the flowers had to be made during the old man's eight-hour-a-day tenancy of the shelf, because this was the family's only period and place of shelter, the rest of the time they lived in the street, and, in the street, sudden rain might spoil the work.

They tried to sell me the finished flower; with dignity, however, not pestering me to buy. In this dreadful place I should not have dared to buy anything, for fear of being mobbed, and had left my handbag behind. When I showed that I had empty hands, the older people stopped pressing me: only the children begged on, hopelessly: 'Cumshaw!' 'Cumshaw!'

I followed wash-amah upstairs, feeling my way in near-darkness over broken steps, between big bundles which stirred slightly as my foot touched them. Day-sleepers could get accommodation slightly cheaper. The walls I groped along were of wood turned slimy in decay. Underfoot it was occasionally slippery, too, with dirt I could smell but not see. I became afraid of being sick, then and there.

On the landings, conditions were a little better: the people who lived at either end of the floor had light from the windows. There were no rooms, but those who had pieces of tattered blanket and sacking to spare, or could get hold of wooden boxes, mostly broken tea-chests, made slightly private cubicles for the family living-space. This cut off the light from other people: those in the middle of the floors saw no daylight at all: among them, the relatively well-off paid extra to share the cost of an electric light-bulb, dangling from the ceiling. It served a number of families, and was never put out.

In one of these families, a woman was dressing a child to go to school, taking shoes off one brother and a shirt off another, to make the third respectable. Here was hope: the child was not the family's eldest but the cleverest: wash-amah tapped her forehead with her finger, admiringly. He had been chosen out of five other children as the one who might eventually drag them all up, and out of this house.

These people, I realised, were not refugees as I, in the West, had understood the term, to describe, as a rule, pathetic creatures, gutted by misfortune, who would never again do anything to help themselves, once the refugee spirit took possession of them. These were people, destitute for the moment, on the way to being prosperous elsewhere, somehow, anyhow, ruthlessly. I remembered what Tom Jarvis had said of the vitality of this race. No doubt the group of relatives downstairs who were now combining to make plastic flowers, and would soon embark on a mat, would have others working for them in a month or so, and sweat them, too.

But there were many in this place who plainly had no hope, the crippled, the sick with cavernous faces and listless bodies. Tuberculosis was said to be killing once every seven minutes, in this town.

On another shelf, with a bunk above and a bunk below, an exhausted young woman lay asleep, or drugged – heroin was cheap, I had been told, and though contraband in Hong Kong, easy to come by, smuggled in through Macao from Red China, along with many of the refugees. Her breasts were bare, and evidently dry; an angry, crying baby was crawling over her, pounding at the grimy flesh with a tiny wizened fist. Round her a big, young family milled, noses dripping, pants soiled; I was in no way surprised to hear, later, that the devoted band of voluntary workers running the Family Planning Association in Hong Kong were making little headway in introducing birth-control to the tenements and shantytowns of Kowloon. If a young woman like this had four children and another on the way, and the space of a bed for them all to live in, what difference could it make if she had one more? Life on any reasonably bearable level was unattainable, and copulation provided the only pleasure possible in these circumstances.

My presence was not resented; on the whole, little curiosity was shown in me. From time to time, harassed Government welfare workers must have tried to do what they could here, vainly stemming this ever-rising tide of human need: the visit of a European was likely to be of benefit in some way. A family might be given a place in one of the huge, humming concrete blocks springing up fast but never fast enough, wherever the Government could find or clear a site. Then those left behind in the tenement could expect to encroach a little on the freed space, without the landlord being able to make them pay any more: he was undoubtedly getting as much as he could out of them already.

Most of the questions I wanted to ask would have to wait: wash-amah could not pass them on. One was about the dogs. Why should people, hard put to feed themselves, keep so many – or any at all? Here, as in the New Territory villages, were lean, miserable looking chow bitches, but unexpectedly plump puppies, mixed up with the human young. Their condition and their excrement added to the smell which kept making my stomach heave. But it was not difficult to discover, without asking anyone, that for this shifting population of about eighty to a hundred and fifty inmates, accommodated on three floors, there was only one appalling earth closet in the basement, along with various spittoons, used for all purposes and emptied when convenient. This rough figure of a hundred-odd tenants did not include the roof-squatters. Though I had come specially to see them I never got as far as their dwelling-space.

Water restrictions in force everywhere in Hong Kong meant that, except in a hospital, no tap ran for more than four hours a day: but for us, next door, as in all European or wealthy Chinese houses, there were big storage tanks. These took up room, however, and any space in the tenement could be let. There were no storage tanks, and only one tap, also in the basement.

Women cooked in relays, on charcoal braziers, four to each floor; round them a little crowd, denser than the crowd elsewhere, waited for a turn at the communal pots; but there appeared to be no quarrelling; just as the children never seemed to fight among themselves. Ever since I had arrived in Hong Kong I had marvelled that Chinese children managed to be born good, and wondered if it could be the result of generations of malnutrition.

Malnutrition undoubtedly came into it, I now concluded, but mainly responsible was the ferocity of the competition to survive. Only those who were obedient and co-operative and patient could get through their years of helplessness, against so many handicaps. Until that day I had not known what bed-bugs looked like; I was never doubtful about identifying them again, they were everywhere, in the cracks of the walls, adding, when squashed, a peculiar smell of their own to the complicated stench of poverty.

What I had expected to find, before I looked over this tene-ment, I could not have said afterwards. I knew the Chinese exploited their own people mercilessly, kindness being strictly reserved for the family circle. I had foreseen that the circum-stances of destitution must be worse in enclosed premises than in the New Territory villages, or even the shanty-town above Healthy Valley through which I had once walked with Barney, for they at least had open air around their beast-like lairs. Somehow this shut-in horror was more than I could face. Unlike Barney, I could never find detachment in thinking that someone was to blame: however heroic the efforts of local officials, the sheer number of immigrants brought chaos: and would go on bringing chaos, no-one was conveniently to blame because there was not enough building space, not enough medical inspection, nor hospital accommodation, nothing like enough schools because there were not enough trained teachers. No town, even as prosperous as this one, could care adequately for a million new citizens. I was ashamed, as a human being, because these people lived here, and suddenly I could not force myself to go on, to see the roof-dwellers from near by.

I called the wash-amah, and fled downwards through the

encumbered darkness of the stairs, beyond caring if I accidentally kicked one or two of the sleepers.

A hand caught my shoulder as I passed the first landing. Here, in the light from a window, stood the old woman I had met in the New Territories, the stone-carrier who had tried to tell me something. She was still trying, gabbling away. It might well be the same thing – that she knew by some grape-vine source where I lived, and wanted to make me understand she would be living close by, she and her family. There could be nothing more extraordinary in her knowing something about me than in the little spy being forewarned of the Royal Naval bird-watchers' arrival on the frontier.

Behind the old woman stood the girl who had chopped wood: not smiling now. She had a fierce, determined little face, seen from near by. Not only her teeth suggested a fox's mask.

'Yes, yes,' I said, freeing myself brusquely, unwilling to take a breath more than I must of this thick air, but the girl held out a pamphlet and enunciated very carefully and distinctly, 'How to say?', pointing to one page. I took the thing from her and looked at it. Dog-eared and torn, it was one of the booklets given away by tourist bureaux, with advertisements disguised as useful shopping suggestions, lists of banks and consulates, and half a page of phrases for the visitor to try, English written one side, Cantonese the other. This copy must have been very old, because one sentence which I left out while reading the rest was, 'Bring me some muffins.' Not since the war, I fancied, had anyone ordered muffins in Hong Kong: the girl had no need of those words. Reading the Cantonese beside me, she noticed the omission and tapped the phrase insistently with her broken, black-rimmed nail. 'Bring me some muf-fins,' I said obediently, and having given my brief English lesson, fled on, out of the tenement into the street where I could gulp the dusty air, and so back into our house, which suddenly looked quite palatial.

Despite Ah Lee's protest, wash-amah was pushed firmly by me into Barney's bathroom, before I hurried into my own to do exactly what I had said I would, drop everything I had worn in the tenement in a shunned heap on the floor, have a bath, pick the heap up in a towel to throw into the water. It took me a long time to feel clean again.

I asked Ah Lee about the dogs as soon as I could: what could induce families to share still further their low food-supplies? Were the animals, I suggested, perhaps kept to eat? I had some vague impression that 'chow' was also the Chinese word for food. It would have seemed to me, no dog-lover, a very sensible reason for their maintenance.

Ah Lee said distantly, 'We not barbarians, Missee! May not poor people love dog for dog's sake?' and I was abashed, though also puzzled. Nothing I had seen along Kennedy Quay, where the red junks unloaded cargoes of live pigs in wicker baskets, stacking them like crates, careless of what happened to protruding legs, suggested that there was any tenderness for animals innate in the Chinese character.

Not till the next time I met Tom Jarvis did I discover that dog was considered a delicacy only for men: women and children rarely got a taste. Light came to me through some observation he made about the likeness between the Chinese and the Irish in their habit of giving the answer which they thought would suit the listener. I asked if his workmen ate dog. Whenever they could, he said. Dog was supposed to increase a man's virility.

Of course the dogs were bred and kept in the tenement to eat. Ah Lee must have thought that as an Englishwoman, new to the East, I should be shocked by this, almost the only fact about this place which was not distressing to recall. Even in nightmare surroundings, where children were a curse, the male Chinese obsession with sexual prowess went on.

I washed my hair twice within an hour or two of getting out of the house next door. I kept imagining that I could feel something crawling on my scalp. Barney came in to lunch while I was on the second rinse. He rarely appeared in the middle of the day, but was to see someone in Kowloon early in the afternoon.

'Post in. Several letters for you,' he called through the bathroom door.

'Local, or from England?'

'Oh, mostly local. Invitations, I think. One airgraph. Look, Chloe, do hurry and get lunch over. There's something I want to talk over with you, about the office.'

I ceased to worry over anything connected with my neighbours. Not that I was anxious, then, about Barney at the office. But whose was the airgraph, presumably from England? I began rolling my hair up into a bun, still wet, angry with my hands for shaking.

Clive and I had agreed when we parted that we would not write. We were both old enough to recognize the futility of trying to keep in touch, by letters which would grow fewer and more and more difficult to write, as our lives diverged, until all communication petered out, unworthily. And yet I never left the house, nor came into it, without looking to see if anything had come, stupidly hoping that he had weakened.

When I was going out and the postman happened to be late, I loitered about until he came, and I knew that there was nothing. But this airgraph proved to be a letter of my own, returned to me by the address on the back: Barney had not noticed that.

I had written to Johnny, when I had been in Hong Kong long enough to get my bearings, dropping into an account of my new surroundings, which I tried to make as interesting as possible – the apparent reason for the letter – another plea that he should go on with speech-therapy, never mind with whom, because his progress with me had been so hopeful. Constantly in my mind still was the knowledge that I had done this boy the greatest possible disservice, in breaking down his defences, with every skill I had acquired, by love or training, and then leaving him as soon as he had begun to trust me unwillingly – another manifestation of the woman who could only be relied on to disappear when she was most urgently needed.

My letter was marked: 'Gone Away. No Address.' It must have been in England nearly a month before it was returned, unopened. By whom had those words been written, I wondered? – Paul, in a steady job, was not likely to flit, leaving no trace. Johnny could have done it, in bitter hurt, but this was not his large, formless writing, and if he had been responsible, he would have wished me to know it, as punishment. The housekeeper, who had been hostile from the moment of meeting, disliking something about me personally, or perhaps anything out of Paul's past? Possibly, I thought: but in any case it would be useless to write again. Either the family had really moved, leaving no address, or other letters would be intercepted, as this had been.

During lunch, Barney asked one or two questions about my visit next door, but I could give him none of the information he would have gathered in my place. What did I suppose was the average weekly earnings of a family group of, say, three adults and five children? The proportion of children to adults? I could only say, 'Low . . . High.' People were so rarely average, or living in proportion, as I saw them.

I described the child chosen from the rest as the one to go to school: he already knew the figures of school attendance. One in five had a place, and because of the crisis in education, through the crowding in of refugees, children went only for the morning, or the afternoon, or the evening: there were three separate sessions a day. Devoted teachers were breaking down through overwork.

I tried to tell him of the old man who slept with drawn up knees, but he picked on my words, ' – one of those regrettable plastic flowers.' Why regrettable, if the production helped to

97

reduce want? This was an aesthetic prejudice. One should not judge artistically an effort made in grim circumstances to earn an honest living; and from mention of honesty he passed on to his current office problem, Ah Lee having cleared away and gone to wash up, leaving us alone. The problem was 'cumshaw' – the word I had heard from the begging children. Barney was horrified to discover that the cumshaw system ran right through his staff. Anyone else would have taken this for granted.

'But the little I know of this place, there's never a deal settled that isn't accompanied by a present, big or small. The cumshaw's part of the transaction.'

'It's bribery.'

'Not in a land where it's always expected, and so discounted beforehand. By both sides. Why, the lobster you've just eaten was a cumshaw from the fish stall holder in the market. Sent along by Ah Lee.'

'Then please don't ever accept one again.'

'All right,' I said, well knowing that I should, and furious with Barney for making me so frequently conscious of his sterling worth alongside my cowardice. I should never have the courage to send back a little gift, for fear of causing offence.

'I've called a meeting of the whole staff for Wednesday evening about this business. It's really supposed to be a sort of social get-together. Drinks and so on. But I'll have to say a few words anyway, and I'm going to make it perfectly clear that I will not stand for cumshaws, and then talk about other things. Pleasanter things!'

'What a lovely social get-together you're going to have! Barney, you can't go against local custom. Not successfully, that is.'

'I can try!'

'Yes, you can try. But what's the use? You'll only put a lot of people's backs up.'

'If everyone said that about everything which needed doing, where would the world be?'

'Probably just about where it is now,' I said nastily.

Here was the old problem of compromise, which had fascinated me in the past. How much should good give way to bad, if giving way a little was the price of good getting anywhere at all – as it generally was? Everyone but Barney compromised in almost every war. I admired his intransigence, in theory: I knew I should be supporting him at this moment, in a campaign to introduce probity to a sphere of business where it was plainly scarce, instead of showing that I found this an exasperating effort: indeed, more than a little ridiculous.

He accepted my attitude with forebearance. 'D'you mind being alone on Wednesday evening?' he asked.

'No. Of course not. Why should I?'

'Well, only because now you know the sort of people we have next door. From what you say, some of them must be pretty desperate. We'll have to take better precautions against sneak-thieves. I'll get a double locking device put on the door right away. At present anyone with a skeleton key could open it. And we really must get a move on to find somewhere else to live. It's surprising we haven't found bugs in this place already. All right, if you're sure you don't mind being left – '

'Not in the least.' But when the time came, I was oddly nervous.

For the first time since our big dinner party there were noises on the roof again. By myself in the house, I had no inclination to go up and investigate. It was one of the evenings on which Ah Lee, having discreetly enquired whether we were expecting anyone for drinks, disappeared on an unexplained errand, no doubt helping out the service in someone else's house. Most of our glasses had gone, too, I noticed.

I had told him that we should both be out to dinner. Barney had arranged to eat with a couple of his staff near his office, across the water, before the social gathering – I was profoundly thankful that he had not expected me to go. I had recently discovered for myself a little Mongolian restaurant, on this side of the harbour, which entertained me, and would kill an hour by the slowness of the procedure. This required the customers to do their own cooking, at the table, over a portable charcoal lamp, by dipping strips of raw meat into boiling water with chopsticks. There remained, for me, too many periods when time became the enemy I was not accustomed to kill, idly, and had little skill in killing.

Waiting to cross Nathan Road, I was held up by a stream of wildly driven cars of all sorts. 'David, man, relent!' protested a lilting West Indian voice, after one of them had skidded to a standstill against the curb beside me, when the traffic lights turned red. 'Remember you done got Mrs. Cairns one white picknee aboard!' And there was Laura, in a powerful American roadster, with a young Chinese, all platinum watch and cuff-links, at the wheel.

I recalled that one of Laura's daytime charms for the old ladies at the Irish hotel was that she was bilingual in her own tongue. Hailing originally from Barbados, she could when she pleased, to amuse them, slip into a rollicking Caribbean accent.

She hopped out of the car as soon as we had recognised one another. Wherever I was going to dinner, she insisted, she was coming too. 'You call for me later, huh, at the hotel,' she said, dismissingly, to the young Chinese. 'Maybe about ten?'

He made a complicated gesture, which might have been a nod or a shake of the head, and shot away.

'One of the customers?' I suggested.

'Oh, no, Mrs. Freeborn.' (I had been Chloe when we first knew one another, but now I had the status of an ex-passenger and remained entitled to her glossy respect.) 'You know I'm never off-hand like that with the customers.' I was intrigued again by the way her manner popped in and out of irreproachable respectability whenever she referred to her job. 'He was just someone I met in the Gloucester Lounge, giving me a lift to the Peninsula, across by the car-ferry. I wanted to choke him off without hurting his feelings. I hate hurting people's feelings.'

'I remember you were always very nice that way.'

She gave me her wide-eyed, innocent stare. We were walking towards the restaurant with the turmoil of Kowloon's evening life surging round us, jostling us occasionally, and yet for a moment it was just like being back in Connemara. 'Oh, well, I feel one should be, if one can. To make up a bit for all the beastliness there is around. Anyway, he won't show up again tonight. So I can turn in early, and wake up bright-eyed and girlish. Which is what I want – Tokyo, first thing tomorrow!'

'I was wondering why you were suggesting you had black blood in you?' I said. 'I shouldn't have thought you had.'

'No, I haven't. Not so far as I know. Though, of course, you can't be sure. Not with any family that's been in the West Indies for several generations. But it's extraordinary how it puts the Chinese off, if they think you have. That's if they've been educated in America, like David Chan. He's an awful driver. I was scared.'

'So I gathered.'

'Isn't it funny, though, that they should mind, if I let them think I'm coloured, but it doesn't show? They're awfully race-conscious, the Chinese. All right to be yellow, or white, though not really so good to be white. Nothing else will do. As soon as he started trying to get serious, on the car-ferry, I started dragging into the conversation how widely our family stretched, in shade. All the way from me to my little sister with peppercorn hair and a charcoal finish. Same parents, I said, wasn't that interesting? You hardly ever found anything like it outside the West Indies.'

'This must have been very difficult to drag into that sort of conversation?'

'Oh, well, I just dragged it in, anyhow. I think he was too surprised to notice. They're very choosy, you know, the rich locals, about who they're seen with. I expect he thought others might guess even if he hadn't, and then he'd lose face. I'm almost beginning to believe in my dear little dark sister, I've used her so often. I got the tip from another hostess, who really was a bit coloured. Now he'll think he's dropped me, and nobody will mind.'

'Though up to the point of the revelation, "he did want it so"?' I said. If this was rather a tactless reminder of the past, she took it blithely, showing me again those neat little teeth, the persistent whiteness of which had changed her life.

'I told you, I've given all that up. Except when I'm on leave. Real, long leave, I mean, back home. Not just between flights like this. Anyway, he's disposed of. Now, are you terribly good with chopsticks yet, because I'm not?'

Neither of us being adept with chopsticks, we came quicker than we should have done, with more dexterity, to the finale of a Mongolian meal, the rich soup, made of all the little slivers of meat which had dropped by mistake into the boiling water, while we were trying to cook them over the brazier. Laura shovelled in as well the vegetables remaining in half a dozen little dishes on the table. 'This has been grand,' she said. 'I mean, meeting you, and the dinner, too. Now I'll be able to put in eight hours' good sleep before I go on duty. That's what I like.' The dedicated look glazed her again. 'Aren't I incredibly lucky. Here tonight, and Tokyo tomorrow!'

From the very little I had seen of air travel, I could not understand why this air-stewardess job was regarded as so immensely desirable, by girls like Laura. Listening to her talk, it was evident that all places were in fact much alike to her; she spent so little time in each that the whole world was an extended airfield, full of crew-rooms, waiting rooms, herds of passengers, and the same sort of chance acquaintances everywhere, but she was so reverent about it all that I felt as she did about hurting feelings, I could not possibly say anything which might be taken disparagingly.

We finished the soup, and sauntered together as far as the Peninsula Hotel. She was right, it was well past ten when we arrived there, and enquired at the reception desk whether anyone had called for her or not. The rich Chinese youth had not reappeared.

Through the dark side-streets I went back towards our empty house alone, but considerably more cheerful than I had been feeling when I set out. A burst of fire-crackers went off near by, and I jumped as if I had been struck: passers-by laughed, and I laughed back. Long sight, and the street-lamp outside our house, enabled me to see Mrs. Kenderdine coming out of her place, and turning in my direction, before she could possibly identify me. I turned smartly into a side-turning, and let her pass. After the gaiety of Laura, I was in no mood to risk another crying-session in our sitting room: Mr. Kenderdine, I knew, was going on from the Philippines to Burma: in Burma there were dacoits, as well as rabies.

Within a few minutes of letting myself into the house, with two different keys, past the double lock affixed that afternoon, I was thoroughly sorry for my hardness of heart. Even Mrs. Kenderdine's tearful presence would have been a blessing. The sounds from the roof were not to be ignored now. Someone was tapping on the trap-door, deliberately knocking to draw attention.

I froze with fear, uncertain what to do. How long this had been going on, I had, of course, no means of knowing: probably only a little while, otherwise whoever was tapping would have realised that the house was empty, or else adamant against answering the signal.

With relief I heard the tapping stop, and then it started again, more urgently.

103

I went up, with a torch in my hand, and undid the bolts, wondering if I were asking to have my throat cut. As Barney had realised, people of the kind I had seen next door had little to lose and every incentive to take what they needed, if necessary by violence, obliterating the witness against them.

There stood the wood-cutting girl, with an empty pannikin in her hand. She said slowly, in the exact tones of the phrase I had read for her, 'Bring me some – ', paused, and held out the pannikin. 'Wow-ter?'

'Water?' I was incredulous that this, not food or money, was what she wanted.

'Water,' she repeated, as if at a lesson.

I saw there was blood on her hand, and some on her trousers.

'You mean, for you to drink?' The pannikin would hold about a cupful. 'You don't want more than that?' I tried to indicate something bigger.

She understood and agreed the word 'drink': it came into the phrases she had studied, but the rest of what I said passed her by, and once more she pushed the pannikin at me.

I filled it for her in the laundry room on our top floor. It was socially impossible, I found, to bolt the door between us while I did it, but she did not follow me in.

A cry – low, not much more than a gasp – came from behind her as I was handing the pannikin back. I shone the torch past her. A woman with a blanket of sacking over the top part of her body was half kneeling, half crouching, on our side of the barrier between our roof and the tenement's, holding on to the wire. There was a gap in this near by, where some of the strands had been unravelled and twisted back. I was dimly aware, beyond the torch-beam, of a row of faces on the further side of the wire. Not all the big family of roof-squatters were there, by any means: birth was too frequent a spectacle hereabouts to arouse much interest, in those not of the woman's family.

104

When my son was born, with difficulty, I was mercifully under an anaesthetic: I had never watched a human birth, natural or otherwise, but it was plain, even to an inexperienced, frightened eye, that this one on my roof had already happened: all was over but the final stage. Blood was on the ground – some, not much – and on the pile of rags over which she knelt. Blood, black in the torch-light, was coming from her, trickling down her legs, under the sacking.

The girl carried the water over to the woman, who let go of the wire with one hand to take the pannikin and drink, and then hauled herself to kneel upright. Together they began pressing and kneeding her stomach, to bring away the placenta. The woman was weeping now, nearing exhaustion but still capable of effort. They seemed very competent. I stood by for a long minute as uselessly as the other spectators. Of the baby I saw nothing. Probably it had been born dead, because a few days later I saw the mother going about without it, and if it had lived it would have been strapped on her back. The little body must have been handed through the wire gap by the girl, before I came up, possibly to the old woman waiting on the other side. It was not likely to be wholly wasted: nothing could be, in that tenement. A still-born child had no spiritual identity and was supposed, I knew, in many faiths, to be born again to the same mother the next time she conceived. Perhaps the unconsidered flesh might feed a dog, which in turn, as I already half-suspected, could feed a human being, who would thereby be helped to cause another child, in the cycle of life to which these people clung with such all-conquering tenacity, in any circumstances.

Observing the woman and the girl – it had occurred to me, somewhat late, that if I shone the torch steadily on the working hands, I might be of slight assistance – I thought that they and their race were indeed on the way to inherit the earth! Tom Jarvis was right. A small pannikin of water was all that had been required of me – I remembered that in the tenement, without storage tanks, no tap would be running at this time of the night, nor for another eight hours to come. No doubt, because of the spaciousness of my roof, it had been a relatively luxurious place for an accouchement: every available inch next door had been annexed by the squatters, who were not likely to yield ground to newcomers, unrelated to them for any reason.

The old stone-carrier from the New Territories climbed nimbly through the barrier: several strands in the complicated tangle had been left in place, and only the top ones cut and bent aside. She took over from the girl, who stretched her back and used to me two of the English words she had newly acquired. Relationships being all-important, they may well have been the first she memorised. 'Modder – dotter – dotter,' she said, to explain the three of them. So it was her own mother she had been delivering.

When the old woman had completed the job, by my torch-light, she called to the girl. This was when I heard her name, Honuong.

They hoisted the woman to her feet between them. I saw that they expected her to climb back through the wire. No-one from the other side offered to bear a hand. All but three or four had disappeared into their shelters. Sleep, I supposed, must be doubly precious when it had to be snatched, wedged among other sleepers. At the time, I thought that this was why all but the woman's family had remained aloof.

'No, she can't do that,' I said. 'Let her lie here. I'll bring up some blankets. I'll try to get a doctor, to see she's all right.' I raised my voice, to reach the roof-squatters. 'Does anyone here understand English? Please tell her to stay where she is, and I'll fetch things. Doctor. Can anyone explain, doctor?'

One by one, the remaining watchers turned away. I shone the weakening torch on myself and tried some ineffective sign-language. I ran down into our house and began collecting blankets. Gorgeous weather ever since we arrived had seen to it that most of the bedding we had brought out by sea was still stowed away in tin trunks, troublesome to open in a hurry. When I got back with an armful, no-one was on our roof. The pile of bloodied rags had been taken away, and where the wire had been tampered with, it had been neatly replaced. I could see no sign of cutting, and only knew the position of the gap by the position of a few dark smears on the cement underfoot.

I telephoned to the nearest hospital, but was not surprised to find that there was no doctor or midwife available to come at once: this sort of thing must be happening every night, all over the congested areas. If I knew the woman's name, said a Chinese voice at the other end of the wire, and exactly where to find her in the tenement, and that she really was in dire condition, a call for an ambulance might be put through to one of the maternity hospitals. I hesitated, feeling silly: of course this was hardly an emergency, by Hong Kong standards. The voice said placidly, 'I expect she will be all right. These coolie women are very strong. If she wished medical attention, she should have arranged for it before. We have a registry kept specially for this purpose,' and with mutual apologies – the hospital sorry to have no-one free, I sorry to have bothered them – we rang off.

I spent the next half hour, till just before Barney's return, swabbing down the roof, while disinclination grew in me to let him know what had happened. Right on top of us, these people had come too close to be included in his general benevolence towards unfortunate human beings in categories. What he would certainly say would be said by every responsible householder in the locality: if the wire barrier had proved inadequate, we must hire one of those venerable guards, employed by the banks and the jewellers.

We owed this to the Kenderdines as well as to ourselves – I saw that. If squatters penetrated our defences, they could be expected to spread further, to the next roof. But I was intensely curious to know what would happen next.

In the end I made a bargain with myself: if he asked me straight out what I had been doing with my evening, I would tell him: that is, if he stopped to listen. If he performed what I thought of privately as his jesting-Pilate act, he could find out for himself, later.

'Not had too dull a time?' Barney said, and told me that he believed his address had gone down better than he had dared to hope, beforehand. The Chinese as well as the English members of his staff seemed to have got the point, without his having to labour it. In fact there had not been any unpleasantness at all. People saw that he meant what he said about cumshaws.

'You depend a lot, don't you,' I said, 'on your Chinese head clerk?'

'What makes you think that? I didn't tell you so, did I?'

'No, and I didn't mean it specially about your business. I've heard this said – oh, everywhere in Hong Kong. That all foreign-managed firms do depend on one local man in the office. As a sort of mediator between races. And between man and man. Explaining the management to the workers, and the other way round.'

'Yes, I suppose that's so. I suppose we do, really.'

'Well, is he happy about the idea of not making a bit on the side?'

Barney said that he did not know if the man, John Chan, was happy, but he thought Chan was convinced that this was how it had to be. 'I spoke pretty carefully, you know, so as not to hurt anyone's "face." Talked about the future, not the past. If necessary I'll put up his salary. In fact, it'd probably be the wise thing to do, at the end of the month, whether he asks for it or not.'

I told him that I had dined, Dutch-treat, with Laura Cairns, partly to excuse myself for having spent money which I had not earned, on myself, in a restaurant, when I could have eaten at home. Barney was adequately generous, and I had a house-keeping allowance of which the balance was supposed to be mine to use in any way I liked; but Ah Lee's stubborn habit of taking all bills to Master to settle made nonsense of the arrangement. I had still not recovered from the awkwardness of renewed dependence.

'Oh, her!' Barney said disparagingly, and then made an effort to be charitable. 'No, one shouldn't be too critical. She's a merry little creature, and good-hearted, and I remember thinking on the trip here, that her job seems to have done a lot for her. Be the making of her, maybe, if she sticks to it.'

'Oh, she'll stick to it,' I said. 'She's absolutely devout to-wards anything connected with her air-line.'

'Good line. Gives excellent service,' he said approvingly. 'I think perhaps we ought to ask her around here. For drinks or something. Next time she flies in. If we're still in this dump! By the way, I sounded Ah Lee, and he's willing to come with us to another place. So we really must get moving.'

'We certainly must,' I said, hoping that we should not find anything suitable just yet. 'By the way, I've been dodging Mrs. Kenderdine in the street.'

'So have I!' said Barney, giving the good, fat, chuckling laugh which made him again, for the moment, the man I had once found congenial enough to marry. 'She's found out I like fishing, and she keeps urging me to help crew the yacht of a friend of hers who once sailed with the Governor himself. I've told her sea-fishing's no good to me. Must be fly. But she says H.E. might be coming on that yacht again. He's keen on cruising. I gather if I played my hooks right, we could even land a dinner at Government House! I'd rather have Laura Cairns around than Mrs. Kenderdine – dear, loving soul that she is! I'm sure no air hostess ever cries into the sherry.'

CHAPTER VIII

'Produce of Hong Kong'

'THOSE PEOPLE ON our roof –' I tried shock tactics on Ah Lee as soon as Barney had left for the office in the morning. 'I don't mean the present lot,' I said, speaking with the utmost casualness, 'but the ones who were there before, when we first came – Where've they gone?'

I knew by this time that in matters of face, any attack which invited a lie for defence was dangerous: not that the lie mattered, but the showing up of the lie demeaned both parties; it was a mannerless manoeuvre. The off-hand assumption of shared knowledge seemed much safer.

'Who, Missee?'

'The squatters who used to eat up our left-overs. Not Honuong and her family, they've only just moved in. Till a few days ago they were living in the New Territories, up near the frontier. That's where I first met them, and I've seen them twice since then. I mean the people I never saw. Only heard sometimes. What's happened to them? If they hadn't gone, this new lot wouldn't have taken their place.'

'They find jobs in Hong Kong itself,' said Ah Lee imperturbably, 'and move across water to live nearer work.'

Good: now we were past the danger point, we could tactfully forget that he had once assured Barney and me we were hearing nothing. 'You found them jobs?' I asked.

'Was able to help, with advice.'

'Relatives of yours, were they?' I suggested. He was unlikely to have helped them otherwise.

'Cousin of my wife's second uncle.'

That, I thought, would not stop the bargain he must have made with them, before we came, being a hard one. He would

110

get his pound of flesh after all, in back-payment for our food: I should have realised before, when I wondered why he looked after them, that with refugees flooding over the border there was bound to be a prevalent form of family blackmail. Those who were already established took a bond on the future of the newly-arrived. And being Chinese, the relatives could be relied on to honour it, in due course.

'I didn't know you had a wife, Ah Lee.'

'She is still in China, with our eldest son. Our two young children are at school here, with the Jesuits in Shauky Wan.'

'You're a Buddhist, though, aren't you?'

'They, also. But this is the best education I can get for them. Very good teaching.' He moved swiftly to attack in his turn. 'Missee, was a mistake to hold the torch for Honuong and the old woman! If I been there, I would warned you!'

'How did you hear what I did?'

'Wash-amah talks to the woman next door whose child goes to the school in Shauky Wan. Honuong told her.'

'Why was it a mistake, Ah Lee?'

'You are involved,' he said, and I nearly laughed. It was true, in a sense which he could not mean. I was devoured by simple human curiosity, and for me there could hardly be a more potent source of involvement, except love.

'Missee don't understand,' he went on with disapproval in his tone. 'You see a road accident here?'

'Have I? No – Yes, a small one. A boy was knocked off his bicycle in Des Vouex Road the other day, but not badly hurt.'

'Would make no difference. Did anyone pick him up?'

'No, people just walked on and left him lying in the road, till a policeman came. I was on a tram and couldn't get to him before the policeman. I thought everyone showed up very badly.'

'All right for policeman to help. This is within his duty. The boy will have no claim on him. No Cantonese would pick him up. If you help anyone when he is suddenly victim of misfortune, he has claim on you for rest of his life.'

'You mean Honuong, and her mother, and her grand-mother, too – they've all got the right, now, to expect me to go on being helpful?' I sounded as abashed as I could at the realisation of my rashness, but was secretly rather pleased.

'Only Honuong. You gave the water to her. What she did with it, that was her help, not yours.'

'Oh, Well. We've got a limited obligation, then. That's better, isn't it? I might have landed us into being kind to all three.'

'We will never get that family off the roof,' he said with gloom. Evidently they were no relations of his, and nothing was to be hoped from any of them, if or when they found their feet commercially at last. 'I think Master not at all glad to hear that.'

'No, he wouldn't be,' I said, and waited.

'He has many worries of his own. More, now, than he knows, maybe. We should not add to them.'

'Very well, let's not,' I suggested amiably, and Ah Lee smiled in my presence for the second time. Dismissing the subject, we went into consultation on what should be bought for lunch, and what for dinner: matters on which my opinion was rarely sought. Prawns or duck, cooked Peking fashion, for the evening, perhaps, when friends were coming in? And for me alone, at midday, rice-birds would be very nice, and cheap, too, at this season.

When he left for the market I ran up to our side of the door on to the roof and listened. The wind in the quarter which brought the dust from the building-sites swirling over us, was blowing in hard, whining gusts: I could hear nothing else except an almost continuous bombardment of crackers in the distance. Something big, such as Tom Jarvis's addition of the runway on Kai Tek airfield, was just about to come under construction.

I opened the door. Honuong sat cross-legged under a sacking shelter, rigged up on our side of the barrier wire. She was sewing diligently. The sacking kept some of the dust off her work.

She looked up, saw me, gave me a small, unsmiling bow, a mere inclination of the head, acknowledging my presence as that of someone who also had a right to be on the roof, and went on sewing. She was affixing tabs from a cardboard box on one side of her, to garments protected by cellophane wrappers piled up in several heaps on her other side. I was interested to notice that of the two, I was the one who seemed less socially at ease. It was difficult to know what the next move ought to be; according to Chinese courtesy. With our lack of a common language, we could talk neither of the weather, nor of last night.

Where she had come through the barrier, the gap was plain to see, once more; the unravelled strands trailed on the roof. While she was here, no doubt she could and would keep off the other roof-squatters, from next door; and equally certainly, when she went back, our frontier would be deftly put in order. But there were signs that she had no intention of leaving for long. By the standards of Hong Kong, where the quieter street corners were cluttered with lean-to shelters no flimsier than this one, her sacking arrangement had a semi-permanent air. One side was attached to the barbs of the highest loops in the barrier, roughly five feet tall. Where it sloped down to the roof, the material was kept taut and weighted down against the wind by lumps of broken concrete, some of them heavy enough to be a strain on arms of such skin and bone as hers. I felt sure that she was not planning to carry that awkward load to and fro through the wire.

Sacking and smashed up concrete happened to be the two commodities in freest supply, locally: the first from buildings going up and the second from those coming down. Nearly all the new skyscrapers changing the outline of the city from week to week were constructed of reinforced concrete, the cement for which was carried to the sites in gunny-bags. Chinese economy being what it was, the bags when emptied were supposed to be counted, stored in safety, and eventually returned by the foreman to the contractors – ever since Tom Jarvis had told me about the family working gangs I had watched building operations in our neighbourhood more attentively. It was obviously impossible for scurrying workers to keep an eye on all the bags, all the time, with people as needy and nimble-fingered as Honuong around.

Nimble-fingered she was, indeed; dexterously opening the cardboard box a slit, down-wind, and extracting a tab without letting in the dust, and the garments were not taken out of their protective coverings at all; she worked with her hands inside the cellophane. It was extraordinary to see the job being done so cleanly, in this filthy wind.

She herself was passably clean by this time, especially round the hands and arms. Tap-water had been running for the last two hours, so that she could wash. The daily water-period was half over already. She kept wiping her hands on a loose square of sacking. Her hair, worn in a short pigtail, was the only part of her which was still noticeably dirty: black as it was, naturally, it looked grey under the blown dust.

The trap-door must not be allowed to bang shut behind me, it could only be opened from inside. I shot the bolts before lowering the flap, so that I had finger-hold to prize it up again when I wanted to go back into the house. While I was seeing to this, I caught a flickering, sideways glance from Honuong, though her head remained bent over her stitching: she was not quite as much in charge of the situation as she wished to appear. I found that flickering glance, with the nervousness it betrayed, a prepossessing weakness.

'You – are – sewing,' I said. However conventionally meaningless the words might be, I had not the nerve to state that she had eaten rice that morning. When she wiped the dust from her eyes with the back of her wrist, the two bones in the forearm could be seen separately, with the skin dipping between them.

' "You are sewing".' A tag was held towards me, sheltered in the palm of her hand. 'How to say?' I did not need to look at it to know the words woven into the tag. I had realised at first glance what work she was doing.

'Produce of Hong Kong,' I told her.

'Ploduce – '

'No. Listen. *Prrr*. Prrroduce.'

Even Ah Lee's adequate English wobbled occasionally on that consonant.

'Produce of Hong Kong,' she said, with no trace of Chinese intonation.

'That's right. At least, that's how to say, "Produce of Hong Kong." But of course this stuff isn't produce of Hong Kong, is it?' I pointed to the pile of garments in cellophane. 'It's from Communist China. From Peking, Swatow, Shanghai.'

I thought the place-names might help her to understand, but she looked perplexed. Here were too many new words, though the facts behind them would not be strange to her. Everyone in Hong Kong knew these particular facts: I thought them funny; Barney and I had recently argued about them, hotly.

Hong Kong being one of the world's few remaining Free Ports, junks from the mainland, flying the Red Flag, brought in daily vast quantities of gorgeous traditional Chinese brocade and handmade lace and exquisite, elaborately embroidered underclothes for women, for which there was not much demand in China among good Communist party-members, or perhaps it was only that there was not supposed to be much demand, and therefore every available bale should be exported, to earn foreign money. Hong Kong's commercial value to Red China, as a clearing-post for trade of all kinds with the West, was the main factor of the Colony's safety.

And as soon as such fabric-goods arrived in Hong Kong, industrious hands like Honuong's sewed misleading tags on to delicate pyjamas and enchanting slips, after which they could be sold to rich tourists, or they went further afield, to receive Commonwealth Preference throughout British-controlled countries, and favoured treatment in America – which I found particularly nice. Barney thought we had no business to connive at unloading Communist goods on our allies: the deception ought to be stopped, if only for the sake of our reputation in trade matters.

Honuong would get a few cents for every twenty garments tagged. This was sweated piece-work, undertaken only by the very poor: the extraordinary thing was that she had managed to get some of it so soon after reaching the city. It was a feat to have persuaded some shopman to trust her with the goods.

Her perplexed look reproached me. 'Never mind, good, good!' I said, indicating the box of tags.

Reaching behind her, she showed me that she had her pamphlet with her. That, too, was held down by a piece of concrete. Blowing the dust off it, she read me the tourist phrases in English. She must have been practising hard, since my visit to the tenement, despite the family emergency. When she reached the muffins, she said, 'Bring me –' and stopped, and giggled, looking up at me sideways again, ' – water.'

'Now, Clo – !' The adjuring inward voice, when I was frightened, had always urged me on towards doing something unpleasant: I had never known it try to hold me back. But suddenly the warning flashed through my mind that though I was already involved, I was not yet hopelessly embroiled in her grim little world. I could let her occupy my roof, and give her left-overs, but remain detached and merely interested, if I held back at this moment. I need not mortgage any part of my affection again. But the itch of a workman's hand for familiar tools was upon me. I had heard my teaching voice come back by habit – it was quite different from my ordinary voice:

Clive used to laugh about that. Here was someone with no speech defect, certainly, but the desire for help in talking. ('Now, Clo, you fool – ! Don't do it.')

I sat down, disregarding the dust, and we held a conversation, entertaining if limited, trying to combine words and sentences of which she could read the Cantonese printed on the other side of the page. At an earlier period, before she slipped across the frontier, she must have had reasonably good schooling; Cantonese was said to take four years for a normally bright child to learn to read and write.

Selected in a far-off day of greater Colonial assurance, the phrases in the pamphlet were all lordly, or scolding. 'Bring me – ' 'That is too expensive, I do not want it.' 'At once!' 'Fetch a rickshaw.' 'Send this to my hotel (today) (tomorrow).'

Honuong was specially amused by one of her own efforts. What she intended to say, I imagined, was, 'Fetch me a rickshaw tomorrow': what she actually said was, 'Fetch me tomollow in a lickshaw.' ('She'll get it, too,' I thought, 'with such ferocious drive behind her!')

I noticed that she looked still more like a young fox when she laughed, at the high-flown idea of herself riding in a rickshaw. There was something distinctly vulpine in those two flawless rows of small pointed teeth.

'You would like me to teach you English? Every day?'

This brought, after a few seconds' thought about the words, a violent shaking of the head by way of assent. I had no illusions about her reasons for wanting lessons. Here was not a mind hungry for knowledge – why should it be? Mastering English was the first step to getting on, in Hong Kong. Knowing English might really fetch tomorrow for her in a rickshaw.

I took her head in my hands. 'Then this is for "Yes", and that is for "No",' and I nodded it and shook it gently. Like a bird's bones, I thought, so fragile and close under the taut skin felt the high cheekbones between my fingers.

117

'I'll get you some rice now,' I said. 'Then I can talk while you eat.' Rice with a little fish, a very little fish, would be safe. Other, richer food might be too heavy for an out-of-practice stomach. And paper I must fetch: and pencils, so that we could draw objects and name them. ('Now, Clo, what have you let yourself in for this time?')

That day the lesson was short: rice took some twenty minutes to cook, Chinese fashion, as Ah Lee had taught me. Something he had said was ringing in my head: I wanted to be downstairs again, with the door to the roof fastened behind me, when he returned from market.

Honuong ate very slowly, as undernourished people do, dry-mouthed; and when she had finished about half of what I had thought a suitable meal for a hungry girl, she emptied the remainder from my pot into her spare piece of sacking; either to save for herself later on in the day, or to take back to her family, I did not ask which. Neither then nor on any sub-sequent occasion did she thank me for a meal, though once or twice, when she felt she was getting on, 'for my good English.'

She pulled the handkerchief out of my sleeve, saying 'Yes? Yes?' and nodding tentatively, to have some means of cleaning her hands before going on with her tagging, tucking it back again afterwards. And when I left, she stood up and bowed, quite ceremoniously this time. I had my uses.

She was sewing hard, to make up for time lost in eating, when I glanced back from the doorway.

'Ah Lee, I've been wondering what you meant,' I said, while he was serving my lunch, 'about my husband having more troubles than he knows of, at present?'

Ah Lee for once was not evasive. I sensed he wanted me to ask – had, indeed, prompted the question.

'Master is very good man. Perhaps too good man. Missee should tell him, not everyone enjoys so much goodness.'

'I've tried that for years. You can't warn him. At least, he won't be warned. What special troubles?'

'Head clerk is my third – no, fourth – ' He stopped to work it out.

'Not another relation!'

'Most distant. Of my brother's wife only. But almost each one in Hong Kong is related to each other one. That is first reason why we come. Head clerk say, Master very kind, but no use with face.'

'Oh dear, I was afraid he wouldn't be.' I felt only a little disloyal, discussing Barney with Ah Lee. If I could understand I might be able to help, though I doubted it. 'It's funny, in a way, isn't it, face was the first thing you heard us talking about, when you spoke to us in the airline coach? I said I thought I should enjoy learning about it here. Master thought he knew, because he had been here before. Is it about cumshaws, this trouble?'

'No – Oh, maybe there is cumshaw trouble with some in office. But not with head clerk. Missee, this is very serious.' Ah Lee was clearly worried. Keeping his job depended on Barney keeping his. 'Sometimes Master calls in head clerk and says, "One of the men in outer office has made mistake in bill. See, this one. Check for yourself." Then head clerk can only say, "Master, total is correct".'

'But when it isn't?' Barney would never be wrong over figures.

'Head clerk is responsible for what all clerks do in outer office. If Master goes on saying, "Now look here, Chan, don't be silly. Two and five don't make eight! Here's the mistake".' – I could hear Barney's unyielding voice saying it: till then, I had not suspected Ah Lee of being such a good mimic: he could copy tones as well as Honuong – 'Head clerk can only go on saying, "There is no mistake," or he must walk out. And it will happen, soon, if Master fails to understand, this is not how to show his man such a mistake.'

'Even when it isn't the man's own mistake?'

'For him – John Chan – it must be his mistake, because it is made by someone under him.'

'This is very complicated.'

'No, Missee, pardon, I cannot see this is complicated. Guests come tonight. If you or I steal something from these guests, Master must feel responsible?'

'Well, yes, in a way.'

'Suppose we steal scarf. If they are Chinese guests, they come to him and say, "This scarf I lose, your wife or your servant has one just like, I have noticed. So of course someone has thought it belongs in this house, and maybe put it away in drawer." And Master says, "That is quite right, and I will find it." Then he is very angry with us, and makes us give up that scarf, for him to take back to friends and say, "Everything was exactly as you thought".'

'And then everyone's happy? Except us?'

'Yes, Missee.'

'Well, I still think it's a bit complicated. What ought my husband to say to the head clerk, and I'll see what I can do to suggest it. Not with much hope, mind you. But tell me anyway.'

'He should say, "I make this total what you make it, Chan," or, " – what the clerk in the outer office thinks." Then he should say, "But you know my arithmetic is terrible".' (Even with Ah Lee's excellent imitation of the voice, I could not hear Barney saying that.) 'It is a very *taipan* thing, Missee, to be not able to add: that is what clerks are for. "But this is very important person," he should say, "to whom I send this bill. And I am most anxious there should be no mistake. So please to check, Chan, yourself – several times if necessary." And then Chan knows there is a mistake, and finds it, and puts it right.'

'I see, and again everyone's happy?'

'That is right,' said Ah Lee, and added in the same breath,

'We should order more rice tomorrow' – presumably to show me that he knew perfectly well what I was up to with Honuong.

'Tell me,' I said, glad to change the subject, 'why did you come over the border illegally? – You did, didn't you? Please understand it doesn't matter to me, one way or the other: I'm just interested.'

'Yes, that is how we came. Missee has seen the terrain–' One of the fascinating things about conversation with Ah Lee was the way his knowledge of English varied from day to day. Sometimes he could steadily refuse to take in what I said, and on other occasions come out with unexpected preciousnesses, like 'terrain.' 'And how impossible it is to keep us out? Lakes in the New Territories, one shore Red China, one shore belonging Hong Kong. Boats both sides. They meet in the middle, and who can see in darkness what pass from one boat to another?'

'Why did you come, without your wife and your eldest son?'

'The Communists would not let them go, and I –'

The front door bell rang. Mrs. Kenderdine was calling on us, unexpectedly: she wanted Barney and me to be the first to know it was all right, her husband was not in Jakarta, where several Europeans had recently been murdered by the Indonesians. A cable had just come from him in Rangoon, where all was quiet at the moment. We had not been aware that there was any question of his being within several hundred miles of Jakarta.

There was no opportunity to talk to Barney, save on household matters, before the dinner-party that night. From his point of view, the people coming were contacts to be cherished. I did my best; Ah Lee, as usual, had gathered some nameless helpers and the food was admirable, but conversationally, the beginning of the evening was ominously dull; nothing sparked between hosts and guests.

After the meal the talk turned on the refugee problem as it affected the finances of the colony; we were entertaining bankers, stockbrokers, and their wives. They knew, almost to a dollar, the cost of the resettlement buildings, housing about two thousand five hundred people in each block, on which the Government was lavishly spending public money. They knew the rise in administration rates, over the past few months. They also knew the value of cheap, plentiful labour, for the prosperity of the place depended on it. 'This is a case of having done the decent thing regardless, and for once it's paid a dividend,' said one.

Another said, 'That's right. D'you know there was actually a shortage of casual labour at the docks at the end of last week? It won't last long, though. Moonless nights coming. There'll be a rush of new hands, in about ten days' time.'

A wife remarked, as though she were observing the habits of some totally different species, 'Extraordinary how keen these refugees are to get here. Come over absolutely without a penny, I'm told,' but her husband contradicted her.

'No, they don't, dear. They usually have a bit of money saved up when they come. But they spend it keeping themselves going till they can get niched into jobs. Usually there's an interval when the Government has to keep them.' He mentioned the average cost per head per month. 'Of course, some of them the Government has to keep forever. The old and the blind and the cured lepers – no-one will employ them, the prejudice lingers. That terrible collection out at North Point Camp, the absolutely unemployable – you haven't seen that yet, have you, Mrs. Freeborn? Well, don't, it'd only depress you. Though the best possible is being done for them all.'

They went into the relative figures of the cost of living for a Chinese coolie's family in Hong Kong and a British artisan's family in Britain, and compared wages; finding, as I expected they would, that everything was really in favour of the coolie.

Money, money, money. They mentioned the increasing sum sent out privately each week from the Colony into Red China, usually via Macao, for the support of relatives whom the illegal immigrants, now in jobs, had left behind: it was a drain on the island's economy. I wondered how much of what we paid him Ah Lee – back in the kitchen, feeding his unhired assistants – sent across the frontier to his wife and son: not quite all he could, I suspected: he had other commitments. Wash-amah might or might not be his niece, but I had long ago concluded that what he had done when he engaged her, on our behalf, was to get a job for his mistress where he could keep an eye on her.

They seemed to know, these guests of ours, everything about this fantastic human influx except what I wanted to know: what made the refugees come, packing themselves into Hong Kong as though the whole of England were trying to get into the Isle of Wight?

'Oh, they don't care for Communism,' I was told, as I had been told before, several times, in answer to the same question. It was the stock reply in Hong Kong. No-one else seemed to think there was anything odd in the idea of a small farmer uprooting himself from his ancestral land for a doctrinal reason. The *Calliope* was not in port at the time, so that Barney's ex-shipmate could not be with us this evening, or I should have been informed again how greatly they appreciated British rule; which came to the same answer.

'But look,' I said, trying doggedly to learn, to understand – these guests of ours were knowledgeable, responsible citizens: they ought to know something about motives – 'illegal immigrants aren't only cutting themselves off from everything they know, by coming here. They must be facing considerable risks, in smuggling themselves out of China?'

Undoubtedly this was so, our principal guest agreed. He was the one to whom I should have been most carefully charming, for Barney's benefit, and he was a large, complacent man, sure to dislike women who argued. If refugees were intercepted and turned back, before they were safely across the border, the Communists could be relied on, he thought, to make life pretty nasty for them in the country which they had tried to leave. 'Must admit I shouldn't care, myself, to have to go on living in Red China after trying to escape from it.'

'Well, then,' I said, aware that I ought to shut up, or change the subject, 'on top of the risks of the journey, and their unwillingness to leave home, there's another deterrent, isn't there? They must know, before they set out, they'll face ghastly poverty here when they've used up the little bit of money they managed to save in order to come. They'll be dependent on charity, either for a while or for keeps, if they don't happen to be lucky, on this side. Do you really think a political prejudice is enough to account for their coming?'

'I'd call disliking Communism something more than a prejudice,' protested the man I was badgering. 'Besides, they believe the streets of Hong Kong are paved with gold, don't you know.'

'They can't,' I said flatly, and saw Barney lowering an eyebrow at me. This was not good-hostess behaviour: his knack of spoiling his own chances really ought not to be shared by his wife. But I was hot in pursuit of some explanation which kept eluding me. I went on: 'You mentioned yourself, when we were talking about their escape routes – ferry from Macao, and sampans on the lakes – there's continual contact between Hong Kong and the mainland. The Free Port conditions would see to that, even if the lay-out of the country didn't.' (I was far too worked up to think of using Ah Lee's delicate 'terrain.') 'And think of all the Red junks coming and going at Kennedy Quay! Their crews must take back reports of what things are like here for new arrivals. Remember what you said about the money flowing out weekly: messages must go with it. Everyone gives me this tale, that over a million people have fled into this town on an intellectual concept, if I mustn't call it a prejudice. And I find it very hard to swallow.'

'Well, I expect the Communists have persecuted most of them. Would you call flying from persecution an intellectual concept?' Plainly, the banker was now as irritated by my persistence as I was by his smugness.

'Most of these illegal immigrants were small farmers before they came here, weren't they?' I said. At the beginning of the meat course, when he was dealing in large statistics, he had committed himself to the statement that 90 per cent of the population of Red China existed by scratching a living from the soil. 'Why should the Communists persecute 90 per cent of the people on whose support they depend, if the regime's to go on? It takes a lot of inducement to prize any farmer, anywhere, off his own acres. In any case, even the worst regime doesn't tend to persecute utterly unimportant people. The sort of family now squatting on the roof – next door,' I had the sense to add, quickly, 'simply wouldn't be worth persecuting.'

'I'm afraid I can't answer your question any better than that,' our guest said stiffly, and turned to the woman on his other side, a dear little creature, with a habit of asking men who knew things, questions about the things they knew. Shades of the clinic almoner, why could I never learn when to be quiet? Barney was looking as if he would like to hit me, and into this came Laura Cairns. Barney welcomed her as if she were an angel from heaven.

Her plane to Tokyo had turned back with a minor oil-leak: she would not be taking off again till the following morning. With an unexpected free evening on her hands, might she snuggle in, she asked? Might she not: we all clung to her conversationally for the rest of the evening, while she told us the secrets of her job – a reporter from Arcady.

'We had this obstreperous drunk on board, in the First

Class. Expense-account lush, you know. They're the worst. And I thought it was really too bad for the other passengers – I mean, having to put up with him as well as the disappointment of not getting to Japan. So I gave him the treatment. He went out like a light. No more bother.'

'What's the treatment?' asked the principal banker, all interested smiles again.

'Well, you won't tell anyone, will you? Because of course if enough people knew what was coming to them if they pinched our bottoms, we couldn't make it work. We're trained for this,' Laura said, her voice, in the last sentence, taking on its reverent tone.

'Not a word. And I can't imagine any man daring to pinch you gorgeous girls.'

'Well, we meet all sorts. They also start following us back into the serving hatch. That's when we act. Next time the drunk wants a drink we give him a tumbler of practically neat whisky, or whatever he's taking. Then we get the Flight Engineer to whoop up the temperature of the aircraft in that part of the plane – the heating's sectionalised, you know. Of course we explain to the people near by, when we can do it without his hearing, and apologize for temporary inconvenience. But they're generally so pleased to have him put out, they're sweet about it. The sudden heat on top of the drink, and he's unconscious in five minutes. Then we cool the plane down again. We couldn't wake this chap when we touched down at Kai Tek again. Still asleep in a waiting room, I shouldn't wonder.'

'How do you stand with the Corporation, about possibly losing a passenger?'

'Oh, well, if a stewardess calls for the Captain's help, the Line's fairly sure to lose him anyway. It's much better for a girl's prestige,' Laura said, 'just to give the treatment. You see, we're *trained* for that. And for heart-cases too. In case they die on us.'

'Any died on you?'

'Two,' she said, 'and nobody else knew, either time! If we're told beforehand we've got a heart-case – they're always being flown somewhere in a hurry for operations. Well, no, not "always." That's an exaggeration –'

'I thought it probably was!' said another banker, a fat man who looked as if he might have a troublesome heart himself, but he said it kindly. Laura was thawing everyone, with her mixture of gaiety and enthusiasm.

'Well, we do get a lot. And if we know about them, or guess they're dicky types, we put them next the window, at the back, whatever their seating card says. The formula's "This seat has come free, sir, and I think you'll be more comfortable here." Sort of confidential. People love thinking they're being specially favoured. Then when they die, we turn the face to the window, put a blanket round them, and it's extraordinary how the other passengers don't notice. They're always in such a hurry to get out when we land, they just think, "Fancy, someone still asleep!"'

'And the crew take him out later, through the forward hatch?' Barney suggested.

'That's right. We're all *trained* for that.'

'Laura, I think you're the most matter-of-factly gruesome person I've ever known!' I said, surprising her. 'Have another drink? I'm going to!'

'No, thank you, Mrs. Freeborn. We're not supposed to drink within eight hours of take-off. Actually, there's still eight and a half hours now, but I'd better not.'

The evening was a success, after all.

Later, when we were alone, and Barney had been surprisingly mild about my tactlessness, I tried talking to him of what Ah Lee had said. 'Oh, nonsense, Chloe! I'm perfectly polite to our head clerk,' he told me. 'As a matter of fact, we get on very well. They're never his mistakes I point out – He doesn't make any. Well, not small inaccuracies in bills, the sort of thing that gets a company a bad name. He sometimes goes wrong on policy.'

'But he thinks of the clerks' mistakes as his.'

'A lot you know about it! I'm just not going to have sloppiness in the outer office. Instead of minding my business, which I'm really quite capable of doing for myself, I wish you'd concentrate on house hunting. This place is getting on both our nerves. I thought it wouldn't matter where we lived in Hong Kong, but obviously it does – You see, my dear, I can admit myself wrong! There must be something going somewhere, in a better neighbourhood, which people of our kind can afford. The other side of the water. On the island itself.'

'All right, I'll have another scurry-round tomorrow. I'll bother a lot more agents,' I said, resolved to fail, and was rewarded by a compliment from my husband.

'By the way, that's a nice dress you're wearing. First time on, isn't it? Suits you, that Chinese brocade.'

'It's a traditional design, I'm told, from somewhere in the Central Provinces. Called "The bird, the moon, and the cloud." I had this dress made last week in a backroom in Hankow Road, in order to wear it tonight. It was done by a group of three men and two women who tittered round me for about ten minutes, not writing down any measurements, and they had it ready and sent round to the house inside twenty-four hours. Fitting as you see! The cost to you will be £6 when the bill comes. The bolt of brocade it was cut from was labelled "Produce of Hong Kong": I happened to notice when I was choosing the stuff.'

All that evening, no sound had been audible from the roof, but I should have been prepared to bet, had there been anyone to bet with, that directly overhead, Honuong and her family were sleeping, or at any rate, lying and resting as best they could, packed into the shelter. I had a queer, pleasant feeling of companionship, knowing almost for certain that they were there. Barney had been so forgiving, over my social lapse, and

128

so nice about my dress, that I ought to have been ashamed: now that I was no longer paying half our living expenses, it was his roof much more than mine.

CHAPTER IX

Heavenly Shop-girl

IN THE MORNING, as I expected, I found Honuong, her mother, and grandmother installed on the roof.

The old lady was at work teasing threads out of a torn sack and making them into string: she scrambled to her feet before I could make a gesture to stop her and stood bowing and chattering ingratiatingly. Lying in the shelter, the mother went through a token movement towards getting up, but waited for my deprecating patting of the air and lay back, joining in the chatter from a flat position. Each of us said something amiable in her own language. I gathered from their waving of hands in the general direction of the tenement that they were explaining their temporary presence: they had merely come to visit Honuong, on what was regarded at present as her and my side of the wire; they would be going back at once, or whenever I suggested.

From both women came the sideways flickering of eyes I had noticed in Honuong when she was not quite certain whether or not she would be allowed to stay. There were already, however, signs of permanent occupancy in the shelter: occupancy by more than one person – several sacks, slit open to make coverings, the pannikin I had seen before, a bucket with holes punched in the side, which no doubt became a brazier when they could procure wood or charcoal, and had anything to cook. It was unlit at the moment: and a cracked spittoon of formidable size.

Honuong was too busy to greet me, except by a waggle of the head. Standing by the wire barrier, she was re-reeving the strands across the gap, and exchanging abuse, accompanied by graphic rude gestures, with two of the roof-squatters on the other side, their eyes turned longingly on our open spaces. Sign-language for where to put an unwanted suggestion appeared to be international.

She came across to me when they had retired, discomfited, into their hovel, took her rice-bowl from my hand as of right, and with a backward jerk of the head offered for my approval, 'See-lee bastuds! How you say?'

'I say, ba-a-arstards, Honuong, because I'm English. "Bastard" is American. But either will do. The great thing is, you make them stay the other side of the wire.' I did what I could about this with signs. 'See-lee' I let pass for the moment. The 'ee' sound for the short 'i' in English was inevitable, for a while, from a Cantonese speaker. 'Remember, this roof is for you three only. *Only* you three. One, two, three. Mother – daughter – daughter. Finish, no more. Do you understand?'

I kept getting spasms of alarm over what I had done, in accepting the invasion by degrees. If three came, and were tolerated, why not more? Why not the whole family unit, probably enormous in its distant cousinships?

For the first time, that morning, bed-bugs had been found on our premises, two of them; they were killed not by me but by Barney, who reacted with fastidious horror.

'Look here, this settles it! We've got to get out, quickly. Apart from our own point of view, I'm not doing the right thing by the firm, entertaining in such a sordid place.'

I pointed out that one of the firm's men had found the house for us, in the first instance; but that was all very well, Barney argued; we had been in a hurry to come, and he had sent word that he was willing to accept almost anything, temporarily. It was up to us to improve on a makeshift arrangement. After all, the firm was not concerned with the sum he chose to send back to his mother and sister, only with the standard of hospitality he offered to clients. And for the Manager of the Far Eastern Branch of any substantial firm, this place was a disgrace.

I hardly suppose there was any connection between the infiltration of the insects and our roof-squatters. Still, as one increased in numbers, so could the other, at great speed. But my mood of caution failed to last: the pleasure of teaching someone apt and determined to make use of me soon got the better of it. While Honuong ate, giving occasional small handfuls to the others, I settled down between mother and grandmother to join in the string-making: it seemed a matey-er way of teaching than remaining aloof from their activity.

The mother appeared greatly recovered, though still weak and tired: she took the unravelled threads from the old woman and gave them a first twisting, rolling them in one hand, then they went on to Honuong, who tightened the strand, and back to the grandmother, who twisted several thin strings together to make a stouter cord. At intervals, keeping up the supply of thread to occupy the others, the old woman went back to shredding. The remnant of sack was so dilapidated that even by these ingenious people it could be put to no other use. In time, they would have instead, some sort of rope which, I gathered, would hold up the shelter more securely: the dust laden wind was still blowing hard. I was allocated to the shredding, the least skilled part of the process.

Before I started this English lesson, I gave Honuong an illustrated alphabet which I had picked up in Whiteways Bookshop the previous afternoon, charmed to find that these nursery classics differed not at all from generation to generation. Twenty-nine years ago I had learnt my letters from this edition: I recognised all the drawings. 'M' still stood for 'motorcar,' 1907 model, and there was no mention of aeroplanes anywhere. Pointing, I read out, as I had done for my own child, ' "A" is for Apple – "B" is for – '

'Ba-a-arstards!' The black slits of Honuong's eyes shone with triumph in getting her 'a's as broad as mine. The illustration was in fact of a conventional Edwardian small boy in a Norfolk jacket, but Honuong always ignored his obvious respectability when we ran through the alphabet together on subsequent occasions. Eventually, between us, the boy being a bastard became one of those reliable family jokes, unfunny to any outsider.

Coming of a tactile people, the two older women patted my arm frequently, to show equal approval of my progress in shredding, and Honuong's advance in learning, though I remained slow at my chore, which was hard on the fingernails, while she seemed to become sharper and quicker all the time. Not since I had taught Johnny in the last weeks of his attendance at the Clinic, when he was avid for help, his defences down, had I known the deep satisfaction for a teacher of responding to such a pupil, the feeling of knowledge passing from mind to mind, almost without the intervention of words.

The girl herself, having rights over me, ventured on gay criticism, 'You no good, you get no rickshaw.' She translated this to her relatives and they laughed immoderately at the idea of her threatening me. I could never understand how the Chinese acquired the reputation of being impassive, as a race: they responded swiftly, gravely, or cheerfully, to every situation. I enjoyed their company more and more. For Honuong, I was amused to notice, 'rickshaw' remained the symbol of success, even when sophistication was steadily creeping through her.

Shrilling persistently below us in the house the telephone bell ended the long session: Ah Lee must still be out at the market. I went down and found that the call came from Kai Tek airport, on a party line, so that two people could talk to me at once from that end. *Calliope* had come back from shooting practice during the night, Commander Lory had gone to see his friend, the engineer, and both he and Tom Jarvis were asking if I happened to be free that afternoon and would like to observe a prized Hong Kong spectacle. Lory's ship was in for a re-paint, and the sampan families, who took charge of the work from the chipping to the last coat, were due to come swarming aboard in a few hours' time, slinging paint-cradles over the sides, and getting merrily down to a job which had become theirs by tradition. Each vessel had its own families and was never re-painted, in this part of the world, by anyone else. The job was mainly done by girls, and was altogether worth seeing.

I said I should love to come aboard and have a look. We arranged where Jarvis should meet me, and at what time Lory should send a boat ashore for us: it was only when they had rung off that I remembered my promise to Barney to go house-hunting that day with bug-strengthened determination.

I kept my word, in a perfunctory way, by sacrificing lunch to a flurry of urgent telephoning, reminding bored house-agents who had allowed our name to remain on their books for weeks, that it was a long time since they had sent me anything remotely suitable to look at; and between them they produced two addresses, fortunately both in Stanley, which I could reach by bus. I hurried over but found that one flat, though large and fairly cheap, was to be shared with another family: this would be no use for Barney's official entertaining as there was only one possible dining room. At the other place, on top of a modest rent, key-money – not mentioned by the agent – was being demanded for a set of threadbare carpets in designs of the nineteen-twenties, full of meaningless lozenges and cubes in colours so garish, despite fading, that they would give hiccoughs to anyone with quiet tastes. While I was wondering, reluctantly, if we could afford to buy these horrors to throw away, some other and more desperate homeseeker rang up the owner and took the flat unseen, carpets included.

My conscience was clear, or clear enough to let me find my first visit to a warship highly entertaining. Part of my enjoyment – by no means all, but some, at any rate – was due to the pleasure the jolly, pigtail-swinging sampan girls evidently took in being aboard 'their' destroyer again. They were everywhere, about the decks and the hull, getting as much fun out of the situation as the ship's crew, who were standing by with unoccupied time hanging not at all heavily on their hands. Any effort at slap-and-tickle from the men met with hefty retaliation. I saw one wench deliver a crack with a chipper which nearly knocked a sailor into the sea. He had been leaning too far over the rail, trying for the second time to make a souvenir of her hat, the splendid, traditional beehive affair which I had worn in the New Territories.

Lory explained earnestly to my companion and me that the girls resented familiarity because of their particular position in regard to the ship: it was practically incestuous. Not for the first time, I was puzzled by the strange friendships possible between men of widely differing temperaments. Barney liked Lory for the sake of old lang syne: Tom Jarvis thought him a slightly ridiculous blimp but a first-class fellow, too.

After contact with Honuong and her family, it was good to see solid-fleshed workers, to whom the rice-greeting seemed entirely appropriate. A big cluster of sampans, like ducklings round a vast parent bird, swung at the stern of the *Calliope*: Lory told me that these water-born people, whom I had so often watched from the shore, living in their craft in the typhoon shelters, were really a race apart, never or very rarely inter-marrying with the land Chinese. The men were mostly away in the deep-water junks, trading with the Chinese mainland: the sturdy women fished, and took on jobs like this.

From the portholes near the after-end of the destroyer, bundles were being lowered into the flotilla of sampans. The ship's officers looked elsewhere. It was strictly against regulations to give away naval food, but it was also traditional to let 'her' families do the *Calliope's* washing and mending, and payment in kind was preferred by the sampan people to payment in money. Money they received officially for the scraping and painting: also they got money off the refugees they ferried from the mainland, their only contact with land-types such as Honuong. But tinned stores were what they really appreciated.

Cockney and Chinese voices exchanged surreptitious shouts: there were always new matelots on board who did not know the long established Hong Kong joke, and their shipmates could be relied on not to enlighten them just yet. 'Heelo, Jackee-boy!' (Everyone was Jackee-boy to the sampan girls, from the captain to the stokers.) 'You come ashore tonight? You want address most loving girl in Hong Kong? You let down one more teeny butter – ' and then would come the house number on the Peak of some well-established white family whose outraged daughters would later be besieged by puzzled, half-tipsy liberty men. The back-door of Government House was a favourite assignation given to green sailors.

Because we had enjoyed together, on the bird-watchers' outing, the episode of the appreciation of British rule, I told Tom Jarvis, when the Commander was called elsewhere, that I had lost face as a hostess at my own table by badgering people for a more plausible explanation than the usual one, to account for the influx of refugees.

'I don't know why I got so intense about it,' I said. 'No business of mine why they come.' (Was it still no business of mine? With Honuong's family rapidly becoming part of my responsibility? A tiny panic rose and subsided again: just for now it should be no business of mine.) 'I guess I was just irritated by smugness.'

He laughed. 'The funny thing is, that ever since you raised that point I've been wondering myself, off and on, about the explanation. Of course preference for democracy over communism isn't a reasonable motive! Not for people, most of whom can't read. Put like that it sounds damned silly. But the fact is, I can't think of any other adequate way of making what the refugees face, in getting here, seem like sense!'

Here, at least, was someone who did not think he knew. He was such a companionable man that I suddenly found myself telling him about Johnny and his stammer. Not that the boy and his problems had any bearing on what we were saying, but just that he was the patient I was most sorry to have lost. He asked me if I had ever heard a Chinese stammer, while we were talking about the noticeable lack of strain among these people, and I said, no. I refrained, though, from telling him about the strangers on my roof. Emphatically, I had no desire that he should think me a fool.

The October sun shone on the Nine Dragon Hills, and the gay pigtails waggled overside, and altogether I was sorry to leave the ship and go back to our house when the evening mist came up, and the water in the harbour turned violet, just before – hundreds by hundreds – lights began to blaze along the shores: dusk in Hong Kong was almost unbearably beautiful.

Ah Lee and wash-amah were in the kitchen, demurely separated by the table, when I came in. Ah Lee immediately reported with a blank, bland expression that wash-amah could not imagine how I had managed to get two of my dresses so dirty at the back: they were as if Missee had been sitting on the roof.

Then he sent the girl away. Barney was not yet back from the office. Taking my chance to learn something authoritative at last, I said, 'We were interrupted yesterday when you were just going to tell me something I'd very much like to understand. What was it, Ah Lee, that decided you to come across the border, into our territory? And why did you leave your wife and son behind?'

'But I did tell you, Missee, about my wife and son. It was afterwards other Missee – weepy one who has not enough to think about – came in to talk of her husband. Communists would not let all my family go. That is what they often do. Keep one back, so all the time good money goes from here into China.'

'They didn't make it too difficult for you to get out, and come and earn here?'

'No. Not too difficult. It was not easy. But you know, this border cannot be guarded well, everywhere. My first son, though, they sent him to school away from our district. They said he would make good engineer with training. It was so far from anyone of our family, long long way inland, his mother must go and look after him there. That way, we were parted.'

'You think it was done deliberately? Because someone suspected that you might try to get out with the other children?'

'Of course. Someone must have spoken to someone else. Big people.'

'That's terribly cunning and cruel, their holding on to one son!'

'Why, Missee?' Ah Lee said, staggering me with his complete lack of resentment. 'Only what anyone with power would do.'

'Oh, surely not!'

'Always has been that way in China. And like this, money is sure to come from Hong Kong to Communist country,' he said again, as though I were being particularly slow witted, and could not be expected to follow the reasoning. 'Man must keep his family. Maybe one day I see my wife and first son again. I don't know.'

'But then, what made you come? When you couldn't bring the whole lot out together?'

'Over there,' he said impressively, 'they wanted me to help other families! To work for other men's children!' And the enormity of this, from the Chinese point of view, leapt at last into my mind. The worst of Communism, the calculating ruthlessness of the regime towards the individual, he took for granted. When had authority behaved benevolently, in his native land? What he could not accept was the best of the new system, the practical insistence on 'From each, according to his means, to each, according to his need.' Everything we said thereafter, in one of the most repetitive but also one of the most revealing conversations I ever held, kept coming back to the essential difference between us of the outlook on loyalty, which for him ended where it began, in the family circle. He could tolerate the cruelty, not the unselfishness of the present masters of China. No-one was going to force him to behave as though all men were – or ought to be considered – brothers. As I expected, political systems mattered not at all to Ah Lee and his kind, except when they interfered with a man's absolute right and duty to serve his own kin at the expense of everyone else. As to collective effort of any kind – 'Missee, if man cannot say, "This is my rice because I grow it, and I choose not to give any to you just because you are hungry," what is the sense of man growing rice? There, listen! That is Master coming in. I must at once cook rice and not speak of it any more.'

I never talked, subsequently, to any illegal immigrants whom I came to know well enough to question about motives, without getting, in essence, Ah Lee's answers.

We would agree that the system from which they fled was a form of slavery, and then part company in understanding: its essential evils, as seen by the Western eye, were all right in theirs: but the required widening of a man's sense of belonging and obligation to include his neighbour, or work-mates – intolerable.

Later that evening, I controlled myself socially, and though

138

tempted put forward none of the facts I had acquired from Ah Lee when Mr. and Mrs. Kenderdine dropped in unexpectedly for coffee, to show us that he had survived the perils of the air in returning from Burma, and he started laying down the law about ' – our Johnnie Chinaman, a sturdy individualist, mind you, with a real feeling for fair play and the democratic way of life.'

This constant dropping-in of acquaintances, a feature of Hong Kong circles at all levels, would have exasperated me in England, where I wanted time to work in the evenings without interruption. I welcomed it here. Less and less, in this difficult period of our lives together, were Barney and I left to our own resources, conversationally. But when we were, more and more I came to believe, from small references to the past, none conclusive but all pointing one way, that he had known about Clive. And in that case, I thought with a wry sympathy, a pity beyond personal rancour, he must realize, too, that the ending of the affair had not been of my desiring. Had I chosen to stay on in London, I could have supported myself there easily enough – he knew this as well, of course. He could not, then, escape the humiliating truth that I was with him still for the sake of another man. And yet outwardly we were a nice, normal, sociable couple, accepted as quite an asset to the European community. Looking round the Colony, and wondering about other people's private lives, as I always did, I sometimes thought, perhaps we were a nice, normal couple. Who could tell?

This never knowing when friends would come in had nothing but disadvantages for the harbouring of strangers on the roof, undetected. Laura blew along, after her return from Tokyo, on an evening when Barney's old shipmate had also turned up unannounced. She came breathlessly with the information that there was to be a grand fireworks display on our side of the harbour: a local *taipan's* daughter was getting married, and the celebration was due to start at any moment.

What fun it would be, to watch from our roof. She adored fireworks.

Commander Lory said he was all for them, too. Barney agreed. Good idea.

I had even less time to clear off my squatters than Ah Lee had managed to win for his, by fussing about my dark glasses. I told the people in my sitting room, 'Have another drink, all of you, while I fix up a thermos of hot coffee to take with us, and collect some cups. It's getting cold now in the evenings.' I was out of the door and on my way to the roof before anyone had time to say that they did not particuarly want any more coffee: we had just had two cups each. Once I had presumably started on the job of making it, courtesy discouraged them from protesting. 'Get out quickly. Quickly. And quietly!' I said to Honuong. 'Everything over the wire. Back to-morrow.'

Her English was coming along admirably: no explanation was needed. All three leapt to the move. They were used to my emphasising 'Quietly!': I think even the other two recognized this word by now. I had rubbed in the need for avoiding those scratching movements, as soon as I could make myself understood at all.

I managed to stretch the interval to about seven minutes by making Laura and Barney help to cut a round of sandwiches apiece, to go with the coffee. Laura was immaculate in her uniform: off to Calcutta in a few hours' time. I insisted that she should be swaddled in one of my overalls before she was allowed near the butter, and the overall happened not to be where I could lay my hand on it instantly. In vain she protested that she handled food all the time, in planes, without getting herself spotted. I was firm that she must wait for the overall, and sent Ah Lee to get a clean one out of my bedroom. Crowded into the kitchen, we all got into his way when he came back with it: he could have managed coffee and sandwiches in half the time without help.

The roof was empty, and the top strands of the wire replaced when we emerged on to it. In one corner sacks had been left lying over what I afterwards found to be a stain, from the disgusting cracked spittoon which did duty for everything. 'Those wretched roof-squatters from next door,' Barney observed, 'have been chucking rubbish over the barrier.' The Commander I never liked so much, before or after, as when he said to Laura, 'Shouldn't do that, my dear, if I were you. Probably verminous!' She had been idly shifting the sacking with the toe of one of her pretty high-heeled shoes. She desisted.

There was no wind that night, and so no dust: it was pleasant, looking over the city in the flashing darkness. The firework display was magnificent, and went on for over an hour, ending with the set-piece climax of a huge dragon in the sky, breathing a shower of wriggling light-fishes out of its nostrils, before exploding, handsomely. Our party decided that coffee and sandwiches had really been an inspiration of mine – the air was certainly getting chilly after sunset, now that November was nearly upon us.

I could see shadowy figures moving about the hovel on the tenement top: considerable altercation was going on there. Honuong and her family, I thought, could hardly expect to be welcomed for the night after the things the girl had called across the wire from our side. Probably there was some sort of row with the other roof-squatters every time her family went back and forth to the tenement stairs to reach the street. No sign of recognition was made between us, on either side of the barrier.

'Wonderful, how the Chinese always find something to make a clatter about!' said Lory. 'Don't think they ever stop talking. Can you hear this noise right down in the house, Barney?'

'Not only hear it – we've had it so that we've thought it was on our roof!'

Laura – dear Laura! – took over the conversation again. She had removed the overall and was looking particularly de-personalised, so polished that it seemed almost incredible she had ever needed to quell drunks with more than a glance from those delicately shadowed eyes. Lory was visibly impressed with her. She had, as usual, just had an adventure: decorous, but definitely an adventure: on the way back from Japan. Because of something she reported to the captain of the air-craft, and he radioed on, the police had met the plane to arrest a notorious gold and dope smuggler at Kai Tek. She told us all about it, and the approved routine for members of the crew to pass forward their suspicions that one of the passengers might not be all that he seemed.

In the morning, I gave the reinstalled family on our roof a fine new chamber-pot, the most capacious I could find in a Kowloon store. It was highly Victorian, like so many things in the Hong Kong territory, and had a rose decoration round the rim. I banished the insanitary spittoon, it was not to ooze filth on our premises.

My present was received with little cries of admiration, as always, and never put to its intended purpose. It was used to store drinking water in the long dry hours of the rationing period. The spittoon came back, but to placate me it was rele-gated to the back of the shelter, where it was just a bulge in the sacking, between that and the wire: as it was out of sight we could all pretend that there was no other evidence of its presence.

Two aunt-like women, who tittered behind their hands a great deal, had accrued to the family when it reappeared. My heart sank somewhat: the number of squatters was growing, exactly as I feared. But surprisingly, after admiring the pot and patting me extensively, the aunts, if they were aunts, unrove a couple of strands of wire, climbed over and vanished, never to return to us.

The following day I brought a small Cantonese-English

142

dictionary for Honuong. This turned out to be something of a mistake, although from then onwards her vocabulary jumped ahead. No matter how many new words I gave her to learn before we met again, she always knew them when the time came for the lesson: she would go on down the page, reciting by heart, showing off cheerfully. But still another present, coming after the pot and the illustrated alphabet, led the family into looking expectantly each morning to see what I had brought besides the rice. It was uncomfortable to disappoint them. Aware that this was absurd, I found myself racking my brains for small, inexpensive but useful things to bestow. They should be very portable, too, in case they had to be removed in a hurry. If my own money had been involved I could have bought trifles without a care. As it was not, I spent laborious hours repairing the handle of a chipped enamelled saucepan which Ah Lee had rightly thrown away, and putting patches on pants long past service to Barney.

Honuong wore no underclothes above the waist, in this increasingly sharp weather. This could be seen whenever the wind flapped her jacket away from her cotton trousers. Though the days remained sunny, Hong Kong nights in late October and early November were no milder than in England at the same season, though there was less rain. The grandmother made do with layers of sacking under her coolie-suit, and grew bulkier as the cold set in harder. The mother had the remnants of something fancy, a man's wedding shirt perhaps, or a mandarin robe, tucked into her trousers: it had long sleeves, which showed at the wrists where the arms of her jacket were torn. It was so old and greasy a garment that for a long time I failed to notice that there was a just discernable pattern: the bird, the clouds, and the moon.

These people must have come a long way south, from one of the central provinces of China.

I had tried asking Honuong where she lived before the family slipped across the border near the village where I met them, but she could not tell me, or would not tell me.

She had lived on a farm: she knew the name of the nearest small town, but it meant nothing to me, nor to anyone to whom I repeated it, hoping that it would be recognized. She had no idea what the district or province was called: the farm had been her world.

It occurred to me that though she trusted me, to a certain extent, I was probably, in her mind, ranged on the side of authority. It was always safer, for illegal immigrants, that no-one should know from where they hailed. They might be sent back.

The recognition of the material made me ashamed, in a way that I could not have explained, of the ease with which I had acquired my becoming dress of the same stuff. I had ordered it, paid for it, at what must have been a sweated price, with someone else's cash, and then worn it astonishingly soon afterwards: the least I could do was to provide underclothes for these my people.

I put broad shoulder-straps of towelling on the top of the old pants, which I knew would stretch up to Honuong's arm-pits, and made them into adequate, old-fashioned combina-tions for her. The trio had two pairs of straw slippers between them, to be worn by whichever two were to go out that day to fetch the Government's free food issue from the distribu-tion depot: or if the wearer was Honuong, to combine this with pinching sacks and finding sewing work. I provided another pair of bedroom shoes of considerably worn leather, but never saw them in use. They were evidently considered too good for walking about in, and were eventually sold. So was one of the grandmother's gold teeth. It went, leaving a gap in the front, about three weeks after the family came to our roof. The weather turned suddenly bitter, and they needed more charcoal or wood than I managed to smuggle up to them.

A crowned tooth could be better spared from the front

144

than the side, where it was wanted for chewing, but I was touched to see it had gone. No-one had mentioned that they badly wanted more fuel. Parting with this trophy now, instead of leaving it to the family, was something the old woman must have minded greatly, but she smiled and chattered and patted as ever.

Teaching Honuong English, I picked up a little Cantonese without seriously intending this: after three weeks we could chat together freely, though all in the present tense, about most simple things, ho-hoing one another frequently. Nine-tenths of the conversation was in English, and the rest in Cantonese: my part would suddenly raise shrieks of laughter, which were never explained to me. I knew that as with most inflected languages, a word going down when it should have turned up could make a whole phrase grossly obscene, and it seemed a pity that I was not allowed to share the joke.

Laura Cairns' appearance in her trim uniform, with no shining hair out of place, had greatly intrigued Honuong. She referred to 'that fine Missee' several times in the week following the firework display. I had fancied at the time that I could just discern Honuong's lean figure in the shadows, watching intently – in the intervals of her row with the other squatters – not the fireworks but our party, through the wire. Fireworks, though hardly on this scale, were a commonplace in Hong Kong. In Laura she had a mundane pattern. The gloss of the older girl registered at once on this ambitious young eye.

'What she for, that Missee?'

'No, you must say, "What does she do?" ' I corrected pedantically, thinking how much better Honuong's question suited Laura.

Honuong repeated what I said so that I heard my own voice, not hers: then she added a phrase beginning with the two words which she had just learned, and was pleased to be able to use with feeling: 'I bet.'

'I bet she rides rickshaw!'

145

'As a matter of fact she rides aircraft.' I pointed to a plane passing over us at the moment.

'She there?'

'Not in that particular plane. At least I don't think so. She could be. But I rather believe she's a long way off, in Australia.'

'Then, what-does-she-do, in plane? That right?'

'That right' had superseded 'How you say' at the end of almost every sentence, and I missed the earlier version.

'Ho-ho,' I said, and explained Laura's duties as clearly as I could. The mother broke in to ask what I was talking about, and Honuong translated. This was how I learned my Cantonese, listening to the Chinese for what I had just said myself. I heard Laura described in terms I could recognize, as a heavenly shop-girl, and wondered delightedly if the expression would seem absolute sacrilege to her, in her vestal virgin working mood.

'Ho-ho.' The mother no longer showed any ill-effects from the recent birth, and was busy, with the other two, in tabbing newly arrived Communist goods for peaceful penetration as far as Washington, if need be. Honuong seemed to be remarkably successful at scrounging piece-jobs for all three of them, but the next moment she suggested to me, with a protegee's freedom, that I must know someone who needed an amah? Wash-amah, cook-amah, or house-amah, she urged, her mother would be good at any kind of work, and she herself was finding it more and more difficult to secure enough 'Prrroduce of Hong Kong' work for all three of them. Too many refugees were begging to do this, cheaper and cheaper.

I said I would see if I could hear of anything, and thought of Mrs. Kenderdine, but hesitated. Mrs. Kenderdine was for ever complaining that her present amah was no good and 'squeezed' beyond the accepted proportion. I was pretty sure that with Honuong behind her, the mother would squeeze even harder.

'You speak big Missee other side you? Say, very good

amah,' Honuong persisted, as if reading my thoughts. 'Missee wet-face,' she elaborated anxiously, in case I had not identified her. 'You say, very, *very* good amah?'

'But how do I know if your mother is any good as an amah?' I protested.

'You see, in your house!'

'I can't do that. Ah Lee wouldn't like it.' This was accepted as final somewhat to my surprise, till I remembered that Ah Lee was a man.

'Never mind, you say, and after, she make so!' Honuong gave me her vixen-look, followed by her strangely attractive grin.

'All right, I'll speak to Missee Kenderdine,' I promised weakly. ('Now, Clo – !') 'But mind you, I'm not saying anything about your mother except that she's just someone I've met. Where's your father, by the way?'

'Seellee bastard. Stay China.'

'But why?' I was eager to know whether in his case, too, the Communists had held back one of a family.

'Because seellee bastard,' Honuong explained patiently, and this was as far, then or later, that she would be drawn on the subject of her father. It was astonishing that a Chinese girl, reared in filial piety, could be brought to utter any kind of judgment on a parent, and a sign of her remarkable independence of mind. 'A more thing,' she said.

'You mean, "And another thing".'

'And another thing, heavenly shop-girl' – she used the Cantonese, realising that I had understood. 'What in English?'

'Air hostess.'

It was two mornings after this that Honuong greeted me with a statement which knocked me off balance for a second or two by its staggering assumption that anything she wanted, she would be able to get for herself in time. She must have been working very hard with her dictionary over the more difficult words. 'This night we have much speaking in family,

147

because my mother wish me to become prostitute, but I decide to become air hostess.'

'Then I'm quite sure you'll manage it somehow, my dear,' I said, and on impulse gave her a hug.

She remained rigid within my arm, looking over my shoulder to see what else I had brought with her rice. I let her go. 'Here's a pair of socks,' I said quickly, to cover the slight rebuff. 'One heel's gone, but I daresay you can use them at night when it gets really cold. And I've spoken to Missee Kenderdine. Your mother had better go round to see her at once, because that Missee is going to move soon to the Island. Remember, if you translate for them, to say nothing about this roof. You're just people I met once in the New Territories. Well, that's what you are, really, aren't you? Just someone I saw one day up near the frontier.'

Honuong took the socks and nodded, to show that she understood about the roof. She was admirable, in these days, in the way she always remembered to nod and not shake her head, in agreement.

I heard the echo of a far-off voice saying, 'You get no thanks – ', and my own voice, saying something I meant, and still believed. I had only done what I wanted to do. I had earned no thanks.

It was ridiculous to be hurt.

CHAPTER X

Two Days

THE TWO DAYS after Honuong's announcement of her resolve were full of incident for me, as influential in my life as her decision was in hers.

Barney came back from the office almost rubbing his hands with self-satisfaction. 'Considering I'm tied up all day, and you've nothing to do, it's rather extraordinary I'm the one who's found a flat for us, and taken it!'

'Taken it?'

'Yes. Taken it. I said so.'

Then there was nothing for me to do but pretend to be pleased, and ask the right questions: how many rooms . . . where . . . when?

Two of the naval birdwatchers dropped in within the next half hour to invite us, at the last minute, over to the Yacht Club for a celebration – On the cliff near Collard Point was a fish-eagle's nest, in a regrettably obvious position: the society's members had been keeping an anxious eye on it for some weeks. To hear them talk with jubilation of the hatching, which had just occurred, anyone might suppose they had been taking it in turns to incubate, while the parent birds fished. Less than half a mile away, unfortunately, was the remand-home for Hong Kong's delinquent boys. Two chicks had been reported, appearing conveniently on a Saturday, when the Yacht Club held its weekly dinner dance. As the young eagles' chances of survival seemed to be low, with the delinquent boys allowed out at weekends, it was felt that at least the hatching should be suitably welcomed.

Barney, who loathed dancing, insisted that I, being very fond of it, should go to this party without him. I was only very fond of dancing when in good spirits: the prospect of losing my one present interest, Honuong, was anything but conducive to a dancing mood; but that, I could not say. We had been invited as a pair; if I came alone I should put the numbers wrong, as the bird-watchers had already secured their own women. Someone suggested phoning Tom Jarvis at the air-port, to see if he happened to be free, and borrowed our telephone to do it. In a moment it was arranged that I should go as his partner, and just before we started for the

Yacht Club, I wearing the bird, the moon, and the cloud dress, came the news which infuriated Barney and sent me off with feet on air, ready to dance all night: there had been a gorgeous, heaven-sent, typical Hong Kong muddle with the Kenderdines over that flat. They had not known that we were after it. We had not known they were after it. Hearing that someone had got in a prior offer, they jumped our claim by bribing the landlord to betray us by accepting their higher bid, which he had promptly done, the excellent scoundrel. As Barney said, legally, no doubt, we had the right to sue him, or them, or both, but they still had no idea that we were the people they had wronged, and between ex-neighbours a wrangle of this sort would be altogether too unpleasant: better let the flat go. Dutifully I agreed that there was nothing else for us to do.

After this I danced and danced, with an abandon I had certainly not felt earlier in the evening. Tom Jarvis danced about as well as I did, and was entertaining to talk to, as ever, between dances. The ballroom of the Yacht Club in Hong Kong must be one of the most spectacularly placed in the world, built out over the harbour at the end of a causeway, its walls almost entirely of glass, with the wild glitter of the water-fronts of Kowloon and Hong Kong island curving round it on all sides. It seemed to me that the lights never had glittered so wildly, that the ferries criss-crossing over the dark water were more like caterpillars of light than they had ever been, their swift-crawling legs formed by the reflections from their windows, broken up by the harbour chop. Junk sails drifting by in the night, were irresistible dragons' wings to me: Tom and I argued quite hotly about this. If I had never seen any dragons, he asked, how did I know what sort of wings they had? He had met a tuctu, in Burma, and kimodo, in a Japanese zoo, and neither species had any wings. It seemed enormously important to prove my point, that if there were any but miniature dragons, and if they had wings, these would inevitably be shaped like a junk sail – like the particular sail in the bow of that junk there, glimmering and flashing by turns as the coloured lights from the quay streamed over it.

And suddenly we fell silent and just looked at each other. It was a splendid evening, and I ought to have realised then what was happening, and not put down my sudden, extravagant happiness to the reprieve of our tenancy in Kowloon and my contact with Honuong. So should he have realised, but neither of us did.

I think my lack of recognition was partly because, for me, before this, falling in love had been an unwilling and deeply disturbing surrender of my peace of mind. This was gay. And partly, of course, my blindness was because I wanted not to see, not to spoil the lovely occasion with foreboding.

I drank rather more than I normally did: openly, to the eaglets: secretly, to my roof. Half way through one dance, he and I went out on to the terrace surrounding the club, to see more clearly what was making the red glare on the water in the direction of Happy Valley: or this was why we thought we went.

'Fire in one of the shanty-towns, I expect,' he said. 'My nice old foreman told me, another Government resettlement block is about ready for occupation. The grape-vine puts it around. The poor devils up there on the hillside have probably set fire to their huts in order to be absolutely destitute and homeless and claim priority.'

'I know something about that,' I said. 'You have your foreman, I have Ah Lee. Our personal grape-vines. As about five times more people get burned out than the new block will hold, every time, the situation stays the same, or a bit worse. Poor, poor devils.' It seemed dreadful that anyone, anywhere, should not be as happy as we were, that night.

We stayed outside so long in the jewelled darkness, leaning on the terrace rail watching the unsleeping life of the harbour, that when we went back to the dance floor the others had left.

This we thought curt behaviour, till we noticed that it was long after one o'clock, and if they had waited for us to return they would have lost the last Star Ferry to Kowloon, where one of the other women in the party also lived. They may have supposed we had already gone without saying goodbye in order to catch it, and it was we who were being rather off-hand.

As the ferry had undoubtedly gone by this time, Tom proposed taking me home by walla-walla. But the walla-wallas were just what the name suggested, little motor boats which wallowed their way across the restless stretch of water, between the two halves of the town. A rotten sailor, I was not going to ruin the evening by being sea-sick, and I held out for a ride in a sampan, much slower but less lively in movement.

The sampans available for hire at any hour of the night were convenient floating brothels for those who brought their own companions. Ours was manned by a fat, bawdy old Chinese woman, of great goodwill, who kept letting go of her sweep, its handle held down to the stern by a cord, to adjust the canvas curtain at the back whenever we pushed it aside. We wanted to see out: the scene on the rippled water was exquisite, each wave black in the trough, wearing stars on its crest. She chattered impatient encouragement to Tom, and he refused, laughing, to translate what he could understand.

She seemed surprised when he tipped her, rather lavishly, on the further shore, on top of the regular fare. 'I think she said, "It can't have been worth it," didn't she?' I suggested.

'More or less! Were you guessing, or did you get the words?'

'I've learned a bit of Cantonese since we last met. I hope it was worth it, though? The whole evening?'

'The whole evening? Oh, Chloe.' We were alone on the steps of Kowloon's Peninsula pier. 'Sweet, lovely, lonely Chloe.' He did not answer the question directly.

'Why did you say "lonely"?' I asked, astonished. On the surface, surely my life looked anything but lonely?

'Because I don't see how anyone could be near you and not feel it. Something coming out from you.'

'Well, fortunately, you're wrong about what most people can feel,' I said, hearing my voice go flat and dull. 'Fortunately they don't notice anything of the kind.'

He kissed me very gently, as though we were old friends saying goodbye, not like a lover at all; and we walked on towards my house, not talking much.

The next evening Barney came home looking stunned. His head clerk, John Chan, had walked out.

'I can't understand it,' he kept saying. 'I simply can't understand, why now?'

In a moment of foresight I knew with a shaken heart what was going to happen. Barney could not be making good in this job. Sooner or later, probably much sooner because of this mishap with Chan, he would be replaced and withdrawn. The firm could not afford a Far East manager who failed to get on with his staff, Chinese or white.

And yet it was impossible, as always, not to respect him personally for the reasons of failure: that he was without fear and without guile in his integrity; merely unimaginative about other people's motives, when these were such that they could not move him. Even in this period of relative success he had not lost the knack which had bewildered and exasperated me in the past, of always voicing the uncomfortable truth at most uncomfortable moments, as though by some inner urge towards self-thwarting.

'Has there been trouble about "cumshaws" in the last few days?'

'Oh, a little. But that's nothing to do with the head clerk. It only concerned two of the European salesmen, as a matter of fact.'

'But that would affect the whole atmosphere of the office, I

153

suppose. Oh, Barney, I am sorry.' (For him? Or for myself, I wondered?)

A trap closed round me that evening. In a few months, or it might be only a few weeks, the blow would fall, and he would be just as surprised, then as now. I knew that already. And as the one, if not satisfactory, at least stable ingredient in his life, what could I do but stand by in misfortune? Whatever joy the future held out to me, for kindness' sake, I could not damage him more than he was bound to be hurt by public proof of incompetence. What would happen to us? We should go back, I supposed miserably, to England, where Clive was. I no longer wanted him – the realization came quite suddenly – but in any case I could not fail Barney in disaster, completing the wreckage of all his plans and hopes, and whatever pride he had left to shield himself against the bitterness of getting his chance at last, and proving unequal to it.

Looking ahead, with what seemed horribly clear sight, I saw what seemed that evening the only alternatives in front of me. Either way I stuck to him; that I must do. But I could jog along somehow, filling my life with trivial interests as best I could – after all, most of the married couples we knew, except the adoring Kenderdines, appeared to manage like that. Or I could start upon a series of unsatisfying love affairs, which were likely to grow more and more sordid as I grew older, and perhaps clung to each man longer than his inclination held him to me. And this was ignoble in my eyes, the ultimate shame for a woman, and I would not do it.

Shatteringly upon this, because I was forcing myself to think, not to live in the moment, came the understanding of what Tom Jarvis and I might mean in one another's lives if I were free. But now I could not accept this as a possibility. What could it be, for me, if we bent to love, but the first of more doomed, unworthy, self-deceiving liaisons which would gradually come to mean less and less mentally, more and more physically? But something of importance to me alone, not to the men concerned, for whom it would be a casual bedding down with a conveniently eager woman, who became a bit of a nuisance about it after a time. I had watched this path being walked by other luckless, empty-handed women in the early thirties, like myself. If there was anything in me or outside me to which I could hold on, it should not be the way I went.

'Let's get Ah Lee to forgive us for wasting what I'm sure would be a good dinner,' I said – Ah Lee had just come into the room to lay the table – 'Let's go and eat in one of the fish restaurants off Aberdeen. I'm not a bit hungry yet. By the time we've got out there by ferry, or taxi and sampan, I daresay we'll have an appetite.'

I must get out of the house. See other people moving. Not sit opposite Barney, one on either side of the fireplace, as I could expect to do all the evenings of our joint lives: only not in Hong Kong.

'Food will not spoil,' Ah Lee said pleasantly. 'Missee can eat tomorrow for lunch.'

Barney agreed, and went to ring up a taxi to meet us at the Star Ferry quay on the other side of the water, in half an hour. 'Master has had some bad news,' I said placatingly to Ah Lee while he was out of the room.

'I know.'

By the time we had got out to the floating restaurant, and chosen our fish, hauled up alive in a net from the huge tank over which the eating floors were built, Barney had quite recovered his spirits. He saw nothing more in the incident than the tiresome loss of a head clerk. 'But I can't understand why Chan chose this moment,' he said, returning to the subject again and again, each time with more irritation and less worry. 'Silly fellow, he'd got nearly a month's salary due to him. If he doesn't show up to claim it, we're not going to go chasing after him with it.' And later, 'It's not so far off Chinese New Year now. When every Chinese wants all the money he can get hold of. Only a couple of months. I really don't see – '

Both of us ignored that I had tried to warn him about 'face.' Probably Barney actually did not recall this: he had a remarkably selective memory.

'Oh, well, there it is. Can't be helped. We'll have to advertise the job. You really ought to have had this snapper, Chloe, instead of those eternal prawns. It's excellent.'

'So are my prawns, thank you.'

I liked the wrinkled, old, bare-footed fisherman who presided over the fish-well. I liked the look of the exotic fish he pulled up for my inspection. But I never could enjoy getting on personal terms with anything living which I was about to eat. I felt altogether too much of a murderer if I said, 'I'll have that one,' and saw it immediately handed over to be killed and prepared. So I always elected to eat prawns at the floating restaurants. Prawns were not picked out individually by the customer, and I was interested by the fact that sympathy with living things is closely connected with size. Suffering among insects can be considered without a qualm. The death of prawns, though they were despatched especially for me, left me unmoved. If Barney could have been reduced to the dimensions of a Hong Kong prawn, while he talked on with increasing cheerfulness about Chan – What a nuisance the loss would be at Christmas time, when heavy orders would have to be handled – I think I could have eaten him without compunction that evening.

He said it would be interesting to see whether even an oriental had the nerve to give the firm's name as a reference for a new job, in the circumstances. Probably! And Barney being human-sized, I sat gritting my nails together below the level of the table, in cold pity for both of us.

Again, a considerable fire broke out in one of the shantytowns. It was discolouring the sky with smoke and leaping flames when we came back by the ferry, at midnight. This time it was in the foul Waichit area behind Kowloon. After each blaze, our daily newspaper gave the same explanation:

someone had upset a kerosene lamp: flimsy ply-wood and rags had caught easily, and huddled together, the huts were tinder: hundreds upon hundreds more people were homeless and destitute.

When I went up to the roof on the fourth morning after the fireworks party, the mother had gone, already installed with Mrs. Kenderdine, to help her in the move to the new flat at Repulse Bay; but two cousins had come in her place, one from each of the fire-stricken areas, a frail wisp of an elderly man, and a deaf girl, looking a little younger than Honuong. They had evidently failed in their claim on the new resettlement block.

The signs of the heroin-smoker were on the shrunken body and vacant eye of the man. He had no appetite and would take no more than a few grains of Honuong's proffered rice, accepted out of family politeness, but he was docile and harmless; indeed, useful. He spoke, when he roused himself, good English, with an American accent, and some French and German too, having worked as a porter in a hotel in Peking before the Revolution, when the town was one of the great tourist centres of the East. Thereafter, when Honuong stuck for a word in conversation with me, she turned to him, not to the dictionary. I learnt Cantonese yet faster, hearing the Chinese from her, and immediately the English or some other equivalent from him; but still my rate of advance was nothing to hers. She would soon be ready to try her luck at her interim ambition, a stage on the road to becoming an air hostess. She told me that she wanted to be a sales girl, for several months at least, in a place where Europeans came to buy. In this way she could practise her English, and at the same time the pleasing of the sort of people who would one day be her passengers, she hoped.

It was a good idea, I said. 'Why does your mother want you to be a prostitute?'

'Is immer one in our family. And this one now we have,

she gets old. Not make such money any more. If I go help, she has again money. Plenty, plenty she has, in her good years.'

'She rides rickshaws, eh? In the good years?'

'Maybe two rickshaws, same time!' said Honuong.

The family had now acquired some work in connection with the luxury trade in women's evening bags, the sort of thing Hong Kong exported marvellously cheaply. They strung minute white and gold beads in patterns, and attached the strings to a wire frame; all but the man, who sat and gazed.

'Tell me about the prostitute in the family,' I suggested, partly to set an English exercise, partly from curiosity. 'Where does she work?'

'Not work at all, hardly. Married now. In Macao. But she – my mother's mother – must tell you.' Honuong passed my question on in order to be free herself for the moment, to hold the metal frame between her teeth and knot the strings.

It was the first time I had been enabled to understand the old lady's competent chatter by having an interpreter handy, and it was fascinating. She talked with great gusto: I must have been missing a good deal, at our previous meetings.

Honuong finished the difficult, tying part of her job, and took over the translating at intervals, when the uncle fell into a daze and sat silent for a while. Then the man would come back from his far dream and join in again. Both of them rendered the grandmother's words literally, in the first person, but as the uncle was the only one with a clear idea of past and future tenses in any tongue, the story jumped oddly in time.

'This is the relation of how Third Cousin went away from us, long ago –'

'How we cry, when Third Cousin leaves family house, you call farm. Though I am then child, still I remember how we cry. But more than all, Third Cousin and her father cry . . .'

Questions from me, and consultations about what actually happened, so long ago, when the grandmother was a child, held up the narrative from time to time, but it went forward almost as swiftly as the stringing of the beads.

'Why did they cry? Oh, because it was Chinese New Year. You see? When each man must pay his debts, Madame. If he has honour, he must. You see?'

'And father of Third Cousin, who lives with us, owes much money to a man, and cannot pay. Because he has not it, such money.'

'*Pas assez*, Madame,' said the relative. As a porter, it was probably the foreign phrase he knew best.

'So the father must give Third Cousin, who is young like Honuong at this time, to the man to put in a house of pleasure. So this way the man can take her wages, for little time, to pay debt. It is necessary.'

'One minute,' I said. '*She* thought it was necessary, too? Third Cousin?'

'Of course she *knows* it is necessary. Being New Year, and her father without this money for his debt.'

'Why couldn't the man just use her himself as a concubine, free? To the extent of the debt? Then she'd only have to go – she'd only have *had* to go – ' (this leaping about in tense was confusing me) ' – with one man instead of many.'

The grandmother replied, and the man who had passed on the question, passed on the answer.

'It would be thought wrong. Quite, quite wrong. You see? He must put her in a house of pleasure, and take her wages till the debt is paid. He must never use her himself. This is Cantonese custom.'

The grandmother added something. 'It is honour for us, as Chinese,' Honuong explained, 'that we need not put on paper what is agreed. The father of Third Cousin knows well the man does not take from her one week's wages after he has all his money, and when this is in his hand, Third Cousin is made free to work for herself.'

This was translated to the old lady, who assented patting

159

my arm for emphasis. 'Many, many years she works very, very well.'

'When Third Cousin was free, did she return to the family?' I asked. 'To her father and mother?'

After my question had been referred back there was a small silence of non-comprehension – lack of understanding of my lack of understanding.

'She cannot, of course, return to the family, Madame. At any time. If so, she would bring shame on her father and mother. Because she has been in a house of pleasure.'

'But if he –' The gulf yawned between us. No friendship, no will to understand could bridge it adequately.

Complete severance from the family, for the sake of that family – this was what my coaching, and my rice, and her own driving will to success, were going to save Honuong from facing, with any luck.

'Does it still happen?' I wanted to know. 'This giving of a daughter to pay off a debt?'

Looks were exchanged. Again I had the feeling which had come to me when I asked where the family used to live: that, white, I was considered trustworthy, in some ways, but not in all. The Irishry of the Chinese took over again.

'*Was* Cantonese custom, Madame,' said the ex-porter. 'But British Government here says, no more. So no more. You see?'

'Not in Hong Kong,' Honuong added. And the grand-mother showed all her remaining gold teeth in a grand laugh when this was translated to her.

About a fortnight later, the deaf girl disappeared. One morning she was there, a sad, deferential little presence; and the next, she had gone. Honuong and the porter-uncle turned vague when I asked about her. She was – somewhere, with some other relatives. She would be coming back – soon, per-haps, some day. But she never came back, nor did I learn what happened to her.

CHAPTER XI

The Debt

CHRISTMAS APPROACHED, WITH much festivity. In the shops huge paper Father Christmases appeared, with the snowy whiskers round the juicy-looking red mouths of Germanic tradition, but slanting eyes because the artists were Chinese. I found the effect pleasingly incongruous. 'I think it seems – well – almost blasphemous,' Mrs. Kenderdine said, when she came all the way from Repulse Bay to drop in for a little snivel: not a real good cry, but just a lament that Mr. Kenderdine, though in no danger so far as she knew at the moment, had telegraphed that he must remain where he was, in Singapore, over the holiday.

Ostensibly, she also came to thank me for providing her with an admirable amah. Honuong's mother was proving a domestic treasure. The only drawback to employing her was that an unusual amount of food departed with her on her day out: a really phenomenal amount of food, Mrs. Kenderdine said. I pointed out soothingly that everyone put up with a certain amount of squeeze from Chinese servants, and Mrs. Kenderdine agreed at once that a good amah was almost invaluable and well worth what she took. Still, each time whole packets and tins of this and that vanished unless Mrs. Kenderdine stayed near the store cupboard till the amah left, and even then edible things would be found to have been spirited away, presumably purloined and well hidden before the weekly day out came round. Only food was taken, nothing else. I surmised that shortly there would be several new relatives on our roof, on the principle that mice gather quickly when the crumbs are plentiful.

The pre-Christmas celebrations among the groups we knew

included two occasions on which I could not help encountering Tom Jarvis. I was taking all the precautions I could to avoid this. But we met in a crowd: there was no opportunity for anything beyond cocktail-party talk. When he rang up and urged me to come on another bird-watching expedition in the New Territories, I made excuses at the last minute. There, as on the first occasion, we should have had several hours walking together: more than on that outing because we should inevitably have sought each other out at the start. I knew that I would not be able to help doing that if we were together. Safety lay in not meeting.

If I could avoid seeing him this sudden enchantment would fade, as all such enchantments must, without renewal. Sooner or later, I told myself, his job in Hong Kong would end, and he or I should go back to England with Barney, and that would be the end of it. After all – this was something I recalled whenever the flesh cried out against the spirit – I had met him only three times; really met him to talk to. Put like that, the attraction seemed trivial. With Clive it had been different, a thing of slow growth: I had worked beside him for nearly a year before we became lovers. I was not now a girl, to be swept off my feet by the belief (which might not even be shared! I might merely have imagined it was shared!) that Tom Jarvis and I had both found what we wanted. Had things been otherwise . . . everyone experienced such encounters in life, was passingly aware of a possible love, and nine times out of ten nothing came of it. I had no reason to suppose that even if the recognition had been mutual, it would seem as important to him as to me. He was a man and free, and the whole world was open to him. He had no ties but his job, which he liked: he had told me as much. If only I could avoid seeing him for a while.

On Christmas Day itself I went down with Asian flu, of which the second serious wave had just hit Hong Kong. Flu was complicated by what looked at the time like a minor accident, and I was very ill for three weeks, rather ill for much longer than that.

I woke in the morning with a headache and an unquiet stomach, but believed that this was because I had been dreading the forced jollity of the day: an hour or two later I felt better and went out. The full attack came on with horrid swiftness.

Laura Cairns had breezed into town again and at noon I was in her room at the Peninsula Hotel with a convivial glass in my hand, the first of the day, laughing with her at the transformation in the other exquisitely groomed air hostesses as they came through the door. Quite a number had managed to wangle themselves Christmas in Hong Kong, and were foregathering for a morning drink. Flawless and scarcely human they came, one by one, across the threshold, kicked their high heeled shoes off, subsided on the bed and said something like, 'Darling, remember that fat bastard from Valparaiso, the bottom-pincher? Well, day before yesterday, on the Sydney run, who should be – ' And all at once the glass was on the floor, where it smashed, and I was following it down, down, into sick darkness.

Instinctively I must have put my hand out to save myself as I toppled forward, and cut my thumb on the glass, a gash which went down to the bone. Trained for emergencies, Laura rose briskly to this one, dealt with the blood, almost carried me out of the hotel, and hauled me into a rickshaw, taking no notice of my half-conscious pleas that we should go round by side streets, however long this took, and not down any main road on the way to our house.

She was determined to get me into the hands of a doctor as quickly as possible, and down Nathan Road we went, with the bystanders laughing – I saw them at intervals, between shaming, helpless bouts of sickness – enjoying the sight of the silly white woman, supposedly Christian woman, making a public spectacle of herself so early on Christmas Day. I was afraid, with my last reasonable thoughts for a while, that one person might chance to be in Nathan Road, see me, and believe, too, that I was drunk. Why this should matter, when I had decided not to pursue friendship with that person, I was not fit to worry about, then, nor for days to come. I was given an injection of penicillin as soon as the doctor Laura found for me noticed the depth of the cut on my hand.

I heard my own voice at last, protesting from bed to this bored man, as though he were arguing with me, that I could *not* have been bowled over like that by one cocktail, and anyway I had not even finished it.

'We know that, Mrs. Freeborn! You've been telling us all for a long, long time about your lone gin and French. What we didn't know, unfortunately, is that you're one of the small minority who can't take penicillin. Well, the oedema's over, your temperature's coming down, and about time, too. It's 102 now, it was 104 yesterday, and you were uncomfortably close to 106 for three days. You'll be all right now, but you'd better not try getting out of bed for a while.'

I lay in a dream-like state of near contentment for what seemed an age, just looking at the flowers kind people had sent me. I had very nearly gone out with penicillin poisoning on top of flu. Neither Barney nor I had known, until then, that I had this ferocious allergy to the barbiturates.

Laura had been about to fly home on long leave when I fell ill. With the good-heartedness which had survived her metamorphosis, she put this off for nearly a fortnight to make sure I was going to come through, and look after Barney.

It came to me suddenly that the particularly lovely carnations I had been staring at without emotion of any kind, save mild pleasure, were from Tom Jarvis. I asked Ah Lee when he brought in the milk I lived on. Yes, it had been *that* Master from the airport. He had wanted to leave a note, too, but had been told that I was not yet able to read anything. I think this was when I began getting well. I waited until I knew I should be undisturbed, and then with an enormous effort, hanging on to bits of furniture, battling against nausea and the discovery that my balance had gone, I worked my way across to the flowers and poured away the water into other vases. Dry, they withered almost at once and were removed to be thrown away. I could not bear looking at them any longer.

This particular wave of Asian flu was nothing like as lethal as the first, of whose devastations I had heard from many people. Two years before, it had rolled across China and the neighbouring territories, including Hong Kong, and then passed on into Europe. The backwash, the returning wave which had engulfed me, could hardly be recognized as the same disease, according to the doctor, who turned out to be an amiable man once I stopped boring him with my habitual sobriety. All the same, it seemed formidable enough, I thought, as day after day went by and no new spurt of life came into me.

It had killed on the Peak, among the privileged residents who could afford to live on those airy slopes; it had killed in the best hotels, among the tourists. But in the overcrowded tenements and shanty towns, he said, it had killed no-one except those already dying of tuberculosis. One wave had been enough to teach something in the puny bodies gathered there, how to defeat yet another enemy.

Seeing that I was interested – being interested in anything had once more become difficult for me – he talked about his work as a way of bringing me back into the world. 'These people are practically immune from everything except T.B. They've bred themselves a fantastic resistance. You've seen the places where they live?'

'I have, yes.'

'Then you're one of the few who've bothered. Most visitors, when they first come, walk through one of the shanty towns, as a tourist's experience.' (I felt mildly guilty: this was exactly what I had done.) 'But quite sensibly, they don't go into the huts. When I first set up in practice in Kowloon I thought, "Heaven help me if measles ever gets into one of those tenements! Or any other epidemic. So many under-nourished people, they couldn't recover from chicken-pox. It'll be a massacre." I was straight out from England then, you understand. Salisbury. Wealthy, healthy Salisbury, where every year a score or two of bouncing babies, in well-kept nurseries, die from something quite trivial. Well, I got two bad cases of measles in a hovel where five other children slept. Both got over it, and the others didn't develop it. After that, scarlet fever in one of the tenements, one child and one adult down with a virulent form. It didn't spread.'

'What's behind the immunity?'

'Oh, long lines of ancestors, each one the only survivor of a family bred from another only survivor, back and back. In every generation the rest died young, because they could take infection. That ability has been weeded out. Or very nearly!'

He went away, and Barney came in. Since I fell ill he had been sleeping in a bed put up in our dining room, visiting me at intervals. 'I wonder if you somehow caught the flu germ from the roof-squatters,' he said. 'After all, they were pretty close to us.'

'I shouldn't think so,' I told him, remembering what the doctor had said. 'It was just in the air. Going around. And I happened to be susceptible.'

'I'm not so sure. I wish to goodness we'd managed to move before you went down. For one thing we'd have been saved a campaign with D.D.T.! Ah Lee and I haven't wanted to worry you about this, but we got a regular infestation with bugs just after Christmas. Luckily they didn't get in here, and I think we've coped with them all right now. But I shouldn't be at all surprised if they came with the people up above. They looked a grimy lot.'

I said, 'You mean, the people on the tenement roof?'

'No, ours! I found them there. You didn't hear about it because it was one of the days when you were at your worst. In fact, I don't think you were even conscious. They'd actually cut the wire and put up some sort of shelter. I got them off, and we had an old fellow the Bank recommended on guard there at night for a week to see they didn't come back while the wire was being renewed. It's been reinforced now, with some quite stout steel mesh. Expensive stuff, unfortunately, but I don't think they'll tamper with that. They'd probably need oxy-acetylene gear to do it.'

'Oh. I see.'

'So I let the old man go. But we'll keep an eye on the roof occasionally ourselves.'

'Yes. Perhaps we should.'

'I wonder if they were there, off and on, all the time? From that first occasion when we thought we heard them, d'you remember?'

'Well, if so, they haven't done us any harm, have they?'

'I've just told you about the infestation we've had. You were lucky in here. In the sitting room we had to burn sulphur-candles as well as practically coat the place with D.D.T.'

'I don't believe the things came down from above. I think they came round the walls, in through the windows, or any crack they could find.'

'Now how on earth can you be sure of that?'

We talked desultorily of other things, and presently he went back to the sitting room. I tired easily, and had no wish to chat for long at a time.

During the waking hours of the night I cried, mainly from weakness. And the next morning, too, after he had gone back to the office. Ah Lee, who was an admirable nurse, thought I was asleep and left me alone. I minded that my friends had been driven away. By now I owed them so much. I had given food, and some help, but the indebtedness was on my side.

They had given me more courage and determination than I should have had without them.

These people had taken my heart and mended it: partially, at any rate. Their problems and my problems were infinitely far apart, but compared with their stark necessities mine were easy to face. They had the world to fight. Lying soft and warm, sheltered and well fed and safe, I had only my own inclination.

On the night of realization I had made myself face what the future could bring me: 'The first of a long series of casual affairs, growing . . . I will not go that way.' This was something I had said to myself, but it was as if someone else had said it, with their unyielding spirit, and I had accepted it. And accepted it with less struggle because what I put up with, a comfortable barrenness of mind and body, was so little compared with their appalling endurance on all levels. So I cried, and then lay still, exhausted, troubled lest the mark of tears should still show when the time came for wash-amah to help me along to the bathroom. My sense of balance was one of the things, like zest for living, which seemed obstinately slow in returning.

In the silence there was a tiny, heartening scrape from above: a minute sound, so slight that I might easily have imagined it. I listened intently, minute by minute, and when I had nearly given up hoping, it came again. My roof-squatters had always been good at keeping quiet, unlike Ah Lee's relations: my almost daily warnings had been effective, backed up as they were by bullying from Honuong when necessary. At the moment, someone up there was being doubly careful about noise, after the expulsion.

It was all right. They had come back, or were just coming back. (The porter-uncle, as I discovered later, had just finished putting together the makeshift pair of steps, two short ladders, lashed together at one end, with which they enfranchised the wire barrier with less effort now that it was considerably more solid.)

168

I insisted on getting up that evening for a little while, to have dinner out of bed by way of celebration, and asked Barney to get in touch with Lory to hear what had happened to the little eyasses, the official reason of my former celebration. We were both pleased to find that I could care about such things again. Alas, they had survived three weekends, with evil boys roving free in their vicinity, but not the fourth. The parent birds were reported to be still circling desolately over the empty nest, from which the young would have been ready to fly in another few weeks, calling, calling. Fish-eagles, Lory assured me through Barney, were a law to themselves, and turned domestic at odd seasons: they would no doubt have another brood in due course. But I was sad about the young eagles, and this was my first sign of returning to normality.

For some while after this I did not try to see Honuong. In the early part of January, really cold weather set in, and I had been warned that on no account must I get chilled: ear-ache, which was something I had not known since I was a child, seemed to be one of the lingering after-effects of the poisoning. I stayed in my room. It was enough to know that I was not wholly alone, when no-one else was in the house.

About ten minutes before his usual time of starting for work Barney mentioned one morning that he was just going up on the roof, to make sure that there had been no further encroachment and our strengthened barricade was still intact. I became immediately the demanding invalid, wanting one attention, and then another, till he said a little testily, 'You'll have to get wash-amah to do that. This is one of the days she works for us, isn't it? You see, Chloe, with this inefficient new Head Clerk I've had to promote from the Outer Office, I daren't be late coming in myself. Sets the wrong example.'

'I thought you were going to advertise the job? Get in a man from outside the firm.'

'Tried, I can assure you! Advertised several times in the

South China Daily Post. But the applicants were hopeless. I'm not too happy about this man. Well, we'll see. But I must go.' He hurried off to catch the ferry without inspecting the roof.

An hour or two later, puffing and blowing like a fat elderly woman, and sitting down to rest half way up, I managed the stairs for the first time since Christmas, while Ah Lee was away at market and wash-amah was running an errand for me. Only my head, swathed in a scarf, went out through the trap-door into the keen air: ear-ache had been troubling me more and more.

Like mice, and just as I expected, the number of Honuong's relations encamped on our premises had increased with the supply of food. Thanks to Mrs. Kenderdine, there were now six of them about and it was a miracle that they remained so quiet in their goings and comings. But Honuong herself, the uncle told me, no longer lived there. She had found herself a job, her first as a shop-girl. It was with a seller of *choses anciennes*, the ex-porter said, in Cat Street, where she slept on the premises, under the counter.

The uncle was plainly much the worse for drugs at the moment, and could scarcely pull himself together to speak to me. The grandmother came over and patted my cheek approvingly; by some means she knew about my illness and was congratulating me on surviving it. She talked away, beyond the limits of my Cantonese, telling me of a piece of clothing – mine – hers – Honuong's – Ho-ho, in any case. Very ho-ho, indeed, I gathered.

I cut short the affability. They must all be off the roof before dark. Taking with them every piece of evidence of occupation. Ten to one there would be another inspection, either tonight or early tomorrow morning. I urged the uncle to translate this carefully, and make sure everyone understood that there could be no return until I tied a piece of white rag to the wire as a signal, probably some time tomorrow. If the family were caught here again, the police might be called, I

170

told him. He mumbled something, sunk in stupor. I spoke sharply. (I could not, of course, be sure that Barney would inspect the roof so soon, but he was such a methodical man that having said he would do it, and been prevented, he could almost be relied on to choose the next possible opportunity.)

The uncle mumbled again. I fairly shouted at him, angrily, pointing out that what I had said was important. He roused himself, with dignity, enough to tell me that really it was not important because the family had ceased using the roof at night: it was too cold in the open. The hours of darkness were now spent on the tenement stairs. (I could imagine the conditions: six people huddled together for warmth, not really sleeping, just numb and half-conscious, waiting for dawn.) They only came here by day, to sleep and eat, he repeated. I need not trouble myself with any signal.

Mollified – more than mollified, ashamed of having raised my voice in this mannerless fashion – I withdrew my head and rebolted the trap-door. The luxury of the bed waiting for me was a reproach in itself.

In these slightly shortened winter days, Barney's arrival and departure coincided with the failing and return of daylight. They were safe enough on the roof by day, so long as they crept away before the street lamps shone. Even without Honuong around to boss them they would meticulously, I was sure, hide the hinged ladder cleverly constructed from broken bamboo scaffold poles.

As things turned out, Barney made his inspection aloft that evening, and found nothing untoward. Except by me, no-one was ever caught on our roof again, though from time to time still more of the family collected above our heads, supported about equally by the Government charity hand-out of dried fish and rice, and parcels from Mrs. Kenderdine's.

It would never surprise me to learn that the Chinese, alone of mankind, had mastered the knack known at present, I believe, only to pregnant mice, of keeping their young in their stomachs for an indefinite period, until such time as food becomes plentiful, and then bringing them forth to flourish. Whatever technique makes for survival, this race seems likely to acquire in time.

CHAPTER XII

In Cat Street

JANUARY GAVE WAY to February, and the Seven Dragon Hills were hidden from us for days on end by misty rain: the fogs came early that year. It was nearly March before I felt well enough to go and look for Honuong, on a morning when the world appeared newly washed, and glowing with young spring sunshine.

In Cat Street, where the curio-dealers have their shops, two venerable Chinese men stood side by side, both wearing the long grey winter robes which only a few of the older generation still favoured. Each had a hand under the wide sleeve of the other. They were bargaining in the ancient way, tapping on one another's forearms with talking fingers, not wanting their neighbours and competitors to know the price which was being disputed.

This was for a carved white jade horse held up before their eyes while they argued, by a shop assistant, Honuong in a neat black cheongsam. I recognised the stuff of that garment, an old evening slip of mine I had taken up to the roof, just before Christmas, as a present, with the idea that it would make an extra petticoat for the old lady to wear over her layers of sacking against the cold. Ho-ho, indeed. Between them they had done a creditable job of sewing. Now I knew what she had tried to tell me.

Honuong rotated the horse gently in her hands, first one way, then the other, in order that the sunlight should fall temptingly on its delectable curves and angles. For this purpose it had been brought out of the dim booth behind the two old men, to be shown to perfection: the jade was translucent. It looked to me, though I knew little about such things, a genuine collector's-piece, very old and very lovely. Much of the stuff sold in Cat Street was rubbish, displayed to catch the unwary tourist.

The morning sunlight fell, too, on the girl's intent face. It was sharp still, but it was filling out a little. This was the first time I had seen her looking quite clean all over. She still had the air of a little fox, but now of a sleek, winning little fox.

There came to me one of those moments of heightened pleasure in seeing, when time stands still and the mind is enlarged with the apprehension of beauty. Vixen gazed reverently at horse, and horse looked over its shoulder down the years since it had been artfully contrived out of a lump of greenish stone: in form, both had the grave sweetness and strength of youth, one for so long and the other so briefly. And the old men bargained and bargained, enjoying themselves. They were not grave at all, but tried to hide the satisfied wrinkles round their mouths with their free hands, stroking the few grey hairs on their chins.

That wonderful lance-like early light of Hong Kong struck through the banners covered with Chinese writing which hung as shop-signs outside every establishment: it gilded piled-up baskets of cheap trinkets, so that they appeared magnificent, too, and rested most benevolently on cycles ridden by boys in modern clothes, on the hats of fruit-sellers, running jog-trot to the rhythm of their bending poles: on everything in Cat Street. And then suddenly time slipped forward again at its ordinary pace, no longer keeping suspended in space, for me specially, this precious moment of awareness and vision. The scene became just an ordinary

173

street scene in Hong Kong. Glory departed from Cat Street.

Honuong's eyes flickered sideways at me in a way I remembered: she was nervous lest I should speak to her at once, distracting her from the new role she was acting well.

I busied myself bargaining for something on the bric-a-brac tray outside another shop. In this neighbourhood no-one expected any sensible person to buy on a first visit. Gullible tourists who believed a vase to be Ming simply because the vendor said it was, disturbed him by paying what he asked. If only he had asked more! The old men withdrew their hands from one another's sleeves at last and parted, still smiling, to conclude the transaction on the next occasion, or possibly not then. Honuong carried the splendid little horse back into the shop after her master. Presently, looking through the window, I saw that she was alone behind the counter; he had retreated to the premises in the rear, and I went in to bargain for something. She ran off her new sales patter to me proudly, and broke this off to say softly, 'Missee, I am happy you not any more seek. It was not good when you were seek.'

'No, I'm afraid there was no rice for you. And I'm sorry, too, your family had to move off the roof, for the second time.'

'Was nothing. Only short time. And my mother bring plenty rice instead. It was just not good you were seek.'

'Thank you,' I said, touched. Never before had I seen any sign of affection in Honuong; for me, or for her mother and grandmother. Duty towards her family was different: that was an essential part of her upbringing, not inspired by any personal feeling. Perhaps I had at last been promoted into the sacred circle, I thought, and had become an honorary relative. As if to confirm this, after peering through the bamboo screen across the back of the shop, to make sure the proprietor had his back turned to us and was bending over a ledger, she took my left hand and laid her cheek against the palm for a second, in the charming traditional gesture of a good daughter. I had been over-hasty and clumsy in my approach to her, when I had given her a hug in an easy Western fashion. I should have waited for her advance towards me.

'Missee, no need you buy anything here. Just better we make show.'

'I know. But as a matter of fact there is something I want.'

Barney and I used to play chess in our early married days. We were both medium-good players, evenly matched. There would probably still be evenings to come when I should not have the energy to go out, or entertain people at home. If we could renew interest in the game it might be a help at such times. After some chaffering, I bought the slightly damaged ivory chess set which I had seen in the window from across the road, after I had carefully beaten her down two Hong Kong dollars because a queen had lost an arm, and she had gone to the back of the shop to ratify this reduction with the proprietor. She was delighted, working out on an abacus that her commission would be thirty-five cents (about fivepence). It was her first sale on her own.

I asked her about her wages. Pathetically small, they were: the old man had driven a hard bargain, aware that many thousands of girls in the poorer parts of the town would jump at the opportunity to be fed and housed in the shop. Going about Hong Kong I had often been amazed, when the little stores opened in the morning, by the immaculate appearance of shop-men and girls whose nights must frequently be stormy interludes, since they all slept behind or under or on the same counters.

Honuong considered her first earned money wonderful: her eyes closed into ecstatic slits when she told me the weekly sum.

'You've had a rickshaw ride, I guess?'

She began to shake her head with solemn happiness and then, remembering my training, which had worn off a little because she was working for a Chinese, she turned the shake into a nod, beaming with satisfaction. She had hired a rickshaw to take her from Fire Brigade Building to Radio Hong Kong, a distance of perhaps quarter of a mile. At her destination she had walked into the broadcasting station to ask some unimportant questions of a commissionaire, after pretending to the rickshaw man while she paid him that she had an appointment there, and hoped that she was not keeping too many people waiting by being late. She had managed to keep the commissionaire in conversation till the rickshaw man had looked away, and then she walked back to Cat Street. The ride had cost her a dollar, which was a considerable slice out of her pay, but looking at her while she told me about it, I had no doubt that this extravagance was the most satisfying outlay of money she would ever make, ambitious young creature that she was, in a life which was pretty well bound to be full of wild ups and downs of fortune.

The food she was given in the shop was 'much, too,' she said. 'Good' did not yet apply, quantity was still the only criterion. An exceptionally large meal came with the first and fifteenth day of the month.

Tom Jarvis, it was, who had told me of the duty of shopkeepers of providing specially well for their work-people at the time of the changing of the moon, the dark and the full phase. Tom, who was gay, and interested in other human beings – I must not think of Tom. I would not think of Tom. It was only because he was gay, and I had been so starved of gaiety, first with Barney, and then with the dedicated Clive. These things passed.

'Exactly where do you sleep?' I asked. 'Your uncle said under the counter.'

'He wrong.' The little fox-mask showed its daggerlike incisor teeth in a somewhat wicked grin. 'First night, yes, but not after. Here, Missee,' and she patted the top of the counter, keeping her voice particularly low. 'This way, maybe not very much sleep. Too easy to roll off both ways. But also, easy to hear when someone comes.'

'You mean, the owner of the shop? Your master? He comes?' I disliked the idea very much, because he was old and she was young and so could not want him.

'Ho-ho, no luck for him. Girl more – ' she used the Cantonese for 'eel,' which by the associative quality of the language must also convey, quick and twisty – 'than any old man!' She added pensively the description she used for her father. 'He try once, twice – ' she made a gesture, lifting her knee sharply. 'I laugh. No more tries for him! Just now! So I stay here, one month, two months. Get my sales-talk good as can be. Then bigger place.'

I need not worry on her behalf, I thought. No-one was ever going to get from Honuong, all her life long, any service which was not paid for, one way or another. With her toes curled tightly round the first rung of the ladder to success, she would be all right now. That streak of steel-hardness in her could be relied on to see to it that when her foot slipped off the rung, as it must do sometimes – she had so far to climb to reach her improbable ambition – it would not be long before it found the way on again, a little higher than before. My job for her was almost done. Probably, she would only need me, seriously, once more, in the final stage of the climb, to provide her with recommendation and references. It was pleasant that this was the moment she had chosen for honouring me; pleasant but a little sad. On the way home I reflected, with the easy self-pity which is one of the tiresome by-products of illness, that I really needed Honuong when she no longer needed me.

In the evening, Barney and I played chess with the set I had bought. It had the charming defect, common among Chinese chessmen, that all the pawns were different from one another, and so full of character that it was hard to sacrifice them. Both of us found ourselves hampered by thinking, 'Oh, not that bent coolie! I'd rather move up the squat fisherman.' Ever since my convalescence had reached the stage when I could be up and about, Barney had been extremely kind and considerate. He was one of the people who could not bear illness near him: I fancied he always saw it as some kind of compromise with human weakness. But for the last fortnight he had been more companionable than I remembered for years; in thankfulness, I supposed, that I was no longer an ailing wife: or not obviously an ailing wife. Ear-ache continued intermittently, and I had bouts of giddiness, but these things could be concealed.

There was a possibility, and I recognized it with mixed feelings, partly hope, that we might come together again, come closer at any rate, and make something of our life together.

We discussed carefully impersonal subjects, world affairs, arguing for once without acerbity over the differences in our instinctive attitudes; mine, a readiness to balance a loss with a gain; his, that heart's desire was not worth buying unless it could be bought whole: in essence, it was the old argument again, compromise or no compromise, and as always in courteous disagreement between husband and wife, so much had to be left unsaid, so many telling points thought of but not used, because of their personal implications. It was like playing chess not with a broken-armed queen and two individual pawns, but a queen who could only stride freely about the board one move in three, and pawns which one opponent or the other occasionally pretended were not there. Still, it was our most congenial evening alone together for years.

Amiably he asked my advice about the voluntary social work he had always intended to take up in his spare time: what should it be? It was high time he decided.

Less generous in mood I agreed it was high time: more than high time if he really meant it and was not merely paying lip-service to his conscience. Teaching mathematics, I suggested, figures being his strong point and the need for relief staff being so desperate in every type of school in the Colony. He liked this idea and said, 'I'll tell you what I'll do as well, if I can – I'm going to rake in Mrs. Kenderdine! Do her all the good in the world to have something else to bother about when he's travelling. There must be some subject she can teach. If it's only to keep the toddlers quiet with handcraft, by showing them how to knit kettle-holders.'

'They're quiet already,' I said. 'It'd take a lot more protein in their diet to make Chinese refugee children rumbustious. I agree, though, if you could get her to help distribute food – ' and then I remembered that Mrs. Kenderdine, involuntarily, was already distributing a fair quantity, and finished the sentence by saying, ' – or collecting clothes for the ante-natal clinics, it'd be the kind thing to do. Stop her combing the papers and radio bulletins for disasters.'

'Laura Cairns spotted what was wrong with her,' Barney said, 'when they met for only ten minutes in the hall, while you were ill. Laura came straight out with, "That's a woman who ought never to have any spare time!" It's surprising, really, when you think what a scatter-brained creature she used to be, but Laura's got a pretty good head.'

'She's got a good heart,' I began, 'and various other good bits, but I shouldn't have said it needed – ' and then the room suddenly lurched round me, as it had in the Peninsula Hotel weeks ago. By will, I steadied it, and held it still while Ah Lee came in, bringing us the late post. This had come some time before, but I had not bothered to sort out my letters from Barney's in the hall. I had stopped looking for anything – did not want there to be anything for me.

Tom Jarvis had written to me some time ago, asking me to let him know when I was ready to emerge into life again, and I had answered with one of those vague, dispiriting notes with which friendships peter out. And that, I thought, would be the end of it.

The room gave another, slighter, stagger. The attack would pass, I supposed, and then we would play chess again. I kept my eyes down – the furniture controlled itself better if I did – and considered my share of the mail, a gawdy picture-post-card of Buenos Aires harbour. On the other side was Johnny's writing, telling me that he was now a deckhand on a cattle-boat plying between the Argentine and Brazil. He had scrawled, 'No knowing where I may turn up next!'

By the date, the card had been two months on the way: he had sent it surface-mail. As the address was only my name, and Hong Kong, the wonder was that it had reached me at all, living in a suburb across the water.

I looked up and said, 'Your turn to be White. Want your revenge?' just before the floor rose up and hit me again, and I returned forthwith to long periods of awful sickness.

I did not see Hong Kong again for seven months, except through the window of the ambulance taking me to the air-port, and one brief glimpse of the city from the dockside, towards the end of this period when I was on my way some-where else. So much happened during those seven months that from my point of view I never saw the same Hong Kong again.

My violent reaction to penicillin had indirectly stirred up what must have been an old and dormant infection of the middle-ear. One of the world's notable specialists on Ménière's disease happened to be temporarily in Yokohama: by the pleasant doctor's advice, I was flown at once to Japan.

Later, when the peculiarly maddening pain of this trouble had died down, and I could think coherently again – I was nearly insane for three weeks – it was odd to reflect that had I been stricken in the same way in England, Clive might have been called in, without my deliberately lifting a finger to see him again. When I asked the specialist, a London man, if he happened to know a former colleague and friend of mine in the same line as himself, and mentioned Clive's name, the older consultant showed rare appreciation of the work of an up and coming junior, whom he knew well – rare, in my experience, because eminent doctors were generally as human in jealousy as anyone else, and Clive seemed to have been collecting honours and appointments out of all proportion to his years. Though speaking his name no longer did anything to my nerves and heart, I still wanted to hear how he fared, and I was glad, and perhaps a little proud in a queer, roundabout way, that I could have damaged him by loving him, and had not.

But of the two men I had loved, one dedicated and serious, and the other light of heart, it was the one who saw life through amused eyes, and was naturally a person-watcher, as I was, whom I knew I needed when the days seemed bleakest. The here and now was not easy to enjoy for a long while. I had a feeling of double exile, from the people in my heart and – though less important, how they mattered as substitutes! – the people on my roof.

Even after I was on my feet again, free of vertigo, with my hearing marvellously unimpaired, I was told to stay on in Japan and go somewhere deep in the country, till the peak of the hot weather was over. Climate, and an atmosphere relatively free of germs, made all the difference in this form of ear-trouble: for four months in the summer, Hong Kong, damp as well as exhaustingly hot, was extremely trying to everyone, in normal health or otherwise.

Deep in the blossoming hills, where I ought to have been happy, I lived with a Japanese family, and studied the art of flower-painting, for something to do, between abortive attempts to get in touch with the members of the household. They were polite, withdrawn people, anxious to please but incurious about everything – dim and dull after the Chinese. I never heard anyone laugh heartily in the house, except on the morning when an aunt fell down the well, which was a splendid event because she was a nasty, complaining aunt, and she only fell half-way before being caught by a loop in the bucket-chain. What side-clutching hilarity – not just one guffaw and then cover the mouth with the hand – any family of Hong Kong coolies could have got out of an aunt down a well: even a favourite aunt would have seemed deliciously funny there, to everyone, including the aunt.

Possibly I was unfortunate in my contacts: other European visitors to whom I talked, before and after what I regarded as my imprisonment, liked the Japanese in their domestic aspect. But compared with the variety among Honuong's relations, all the people I met in the flowery hills seemed very much alike, as well as colourless. On the other hand the flowers were lovely, wonderful, the most prolific I had ever seen, and on me, throughout my sentence, completely wasted.

I heard in a Tokyo news-broadcast that the extension to Kai Tek's runway had been completed. Then the personnel connected with the undertaking would have dispersed, to other projects. This was how it should be. Only because I was still a little ill was I devastated by the news which part of me had been waiting almost eagerly to hear, wanting him to have gone, before I returned to Hong Kong. He had not written again: why should he? My note had been placidly discouraging enough.

In one of Barney's letters was a paragraph which I read and re-read before I could take in the full significance. It referred to ' – some boy with a stammer who came round, wanting to see you. An ex-patient of yours, I suppose. I told him where you were, but he said his ship wouldn't be calling anywhere in Japan. He was only in Hong Kong for two days.' My husband's weekly letter took three days to reach me in a secluded valley: Johnny must already have left Hong Kong by the time I heard of his arrival.

Barney went on, 'He seemed to have counted on your being here, and as much as I could make out through his stammer' – I could imagine how it would increase at that moment – 'said something about jumping ship. I warned him pretty straight not to do anything so silly, with the regulations as they are today.'

Poor, poor, Johnny. Was it chance, or a most desperate effort to reach help, that had brought him so far? I could not even guess, through this meagre information, whether it was just the ordinary process of growing up which had enabled him to shed his blazing resentment against me for repeating the pattern of desertion in his early life, or was there some other, adult cause? The one thing I knew was that I had failed him again, by not being in Hong Kong.

The rest of Barney's letter was jubilant. We had moved, in my absence! At last we had a charming place in a neighbourhood he was sure I should like, a tiny house standing in its own garden, overlooking the junk-anchorage in Aberdeen Bay on the other side of Hong Kong island from the city itself. And the rent was no more than we could decently afford. Finding it before it could be snapped up by anyone else had been the result of his new, spare-time activity, teaching arithmetic three evenings a week in a school run for the children of the nine hundred junk fishermen whose families lived in and around the anchorage, mostly afloat. 'So you're partly responsible,' he said generously, 'as you suggested the maths teaching.'

He relieved the regular staff in their fine three-shift battle, lasting sometimes ten hours a day, with the colossal education problem, and being on the spot had brought its own reward. He was knocking at the door, asking to see over the house, while the owner was still nailing up the board saying, 'To Let.'

Mindful of what had happened when the Kenderdine's jumped our claim, he had clinched the deal by rushing some of our gear across from Kowloon, and Ah Lee, with all his mysterious friends, had brought the rest the next day, before anyone could upset the arrangement by a higher offer. 'We're in, and there are no snags that I can see!' Aberdeen was within easy driving distance of his office: he had already found a neighbour with a car who worked only a block away, and drove in every morning: they were sharing the expense, very satisfactorily.

But for anyone without a car, I thought, Aberdeen Bay was a long way from Kowloon: a long, long way from my late neighbours, up above us.

I knew that though Barney had never referred to this in any letter, my illness must have cost him a good deal, and his commitments in England were the same as ever: it was not surprising that he wrote with enthusiasm about built-in cupboards, friendly next-door people unlikely to breed vermin to seep through our walls, and the garden where Ah Lee was already doing marvels. It was sad that I could not share his feeling about my luck in escaping return, at summer's end, to the dingy rooms in Kowloon.

'We got out just in time,' he wrote, underlining our luck. 'The tenement you saw is scheduled to come down, and that goes for our old house and the Kenderdine's, too. The Government has bought the land, paying, I understood, far too much compensation to the old rogue who got the tenement rents, for immediate vacation. Ah Lee, knowing everything as usual, says there's to be another of those resettlement blocks fitted into the space. Demolition starts on the tenement next month. The mess we've been spared!'

So all the ties had broken now.

Where would they go, the remnants of my roof-squatting family? Like the bugs, no doubt they would find new homes somehow, when they must.

I could not bear Japan thereafter. The lack was in me, I accepted, inability to appreciate anything done for me, anything shown to me, if it were done or shown by the Japanese Their formal gardens were undoubtedly charming, their less cultivated countryside etherially pretty with blossom. But it was people who mattered, not places; and in a period of low vitality I fretted to have about me the zest and groundless, irrepressible gaiety of the Chinese. It could not make me more tolerant towards the Japanese to realise that I was being unfair to them.

Recently the specialist had been seeing me only once a month, when I came over to Yokohama for an examination. I persuaded him by letter that he no longer needed to keep an eye on me, so that I might at least move next door to Hong Kong – to Macao, the Portuguese colony only forty-odd miles away. It was easily reached by ferry from Hong Kong, and though just as hot was safer for me, for the time being, than the bustling overcrowded island because it was infinitely sleepy, no-one was building anything, and it was thinly populated: neither dust nor germs would be as inescapable there as in Hong Kong. I stressed, in my appeal, that everyone I had met who knew Macao had assured me that no-one did anything there except watch the world go by, and occasionally play fan-tan. Somewhat grudgingly the specialist gave his blessing to Macao, with the advice that I had better keep out of the fan-tan houses for a while: they were sure to be crowded.

I tore up my stack of incompetent flower-studies with alacrity, wondering over each one how I had brought myself to finish the thing, so abysmally bad they all seemed in the moment of release. The truth was, I had no talent whatever. I gave away paints and brushes to the aunt who had survived the fall down the well. She was the person who had querulously urged me to keep on trying, chiefly, I thought, because she painted flowers much better than I did, and enjoyed my inferiority. She accepted my tools in a disgruntled way, and though she had given no sign of liking me on any previous occasion, behaved as soon as she heard I was going as though my departure were the last straw, after what she had already borne. I made an elaborate excuse about urgent family affairs, paid a fortnight's board in lieu of notice, and within a few hours of receiving the specialist's letter was away in a ship, all Hong Kong bound planes being grounded by fog over the airport. The only way in to Macao, for all but illegal immigrants, was by ferry from Hong Kong. But my ship berthed so near the starting point of the ferry that I need scarcely set foot on the island.

Fog still held Hong Kong when the ship crept into the harbour, shortly after daybreak: all but the quay was hidden: I could see nothing but the dim outline of harbour buildings, and the sirens made my return sound very mournful. I had telegraphed ahead, from Kobe, to warn Barney of my coming, and he met me aboard the ship, bringing Ah Lee with him, to help with my suitcases on the way to the ferry which would leave the same morning. But I had with me only two of those light Hong Kong wicker baskets: Barney and I could easily have managed them between us, without Ah Lee, or we could have found a porter: they were plentiful. I had not seen my husband for months: as it was, we could hold no private conversation of any kind. I wondered if this could be intentional.

'Is everything all right?' I asked Ah Lee, while Barney was absent for ten minutes or so, squaring the authorities because I had no visa for Macao on my passport – These things arrange themselves easily in Hong Kong.

'Is all right – I think. But Missee should come home soon. Very fine new house,' he added as an inducement. I knew well by now that evasive look of Ah Lee's; something was not all right, but I should get nothing out of him by direct questioning.

'I can't come now,' I said. 'At least, I've been told not to by the doctor. Not until October. Unless the cool weather happens to come earlier.'

'Then no doubt is all right as it is,' he said soothingly, and to distract me from probing further, he produced wash-amah's somewhat belated Christmas present: it was now past mid-summer.

He explained that she had planned to give it to me last Christmas morning, but then I had fallen ill. By the time I made my first recovery she had decided to put it by for the following Christmas, and had changed her mind yesterday, when she heard that Ah Lee would be going with Master to meet me. Soon she must leave my service for a while, and wished me to have her gift in order that I should remember her, and take her back in due course. She was going to have a baby in a month or two.

I had never thought of wash-amah as an enterprising girl: for a Chinese, she seemed lacking in personality: but her keepsake was original, and pleased me as much as anything could, on that unsatisfactory morning. She had borrowed one of my handkerchiefs and neatly embroidered a Christmas message on it, 'Hurrah for Jesus,' which was broadminded of her, as a Buddhist. I asked Ah Lee to thank her very much and say that of course she could come back to us when she was ready to work again, but not to hurry.

'This baby, whose is it?' I asked.

'Ah, who can say. Young women today are not like women of old, faithful and good.'

'Will the child be looked after all right, if she hasn't a husband to help her? She isn't married, is she?'

'Not married. Of course the child will be looked after,' he told me with some hauteur. 'Is she not my niece?'

'I have never supposed so,' I said, and saw Ah Lee smile for the third time in our association.

'Ho-ho, Missee! Tomorrow I make offering that cool days come early this year.'

Presently Barney returned, with my permit to enter Macao, and we moved across to the ferry, where I was installed in a chair on deck, with my luggage beside me, and then there was so little to say, the three of us together, that I suggested, 'Look, I'm sure neither of you had a comfortable breakfast, getting up so early to meet me! Don't wait to see the ferry off. I've got everything. I'm told there are always plenty of taxis on the quay at Macao to take people to the hotels. I'll be fine on my own.'

Barney said, 'Oh, no,' in a half hearted manner, 'we'll stay,' but admitted that he was rather hungry. The interruption in our day-to-day contact had robbed us of Hong Kong trivialities to discuss: somehow, all the ground gained in friendship during the first part of my convalescence, in Kowloon, had been lost again. There was one thing, however, that I wanted to make sure of, now that we were face to face, though I knew it, really, already.

'My young patient – the lad who wanted to see me – he hasn't turned up again, I suppose?'

'No, I thought I told you, I gathered there wasn't any chance of his staying around, if he didn't jump ship – and I imagine he was only talking wildly about that to impress me. What a hope! He seemed a pretty crude type.'

'Well, "complicated" is the word, I think. He once bought me a bunch of flowers and pretended he'd stolen it.' I explained about 'oncie-oncieing' for something to say. The hand of my watch crept round. 'Where was he going, if he didn't jump ship? – and I certainly hope he didn't, and doesn't! One way and another he's had enough trouble without making himself any more.'

'Tell you the truth, his stammer was so bad, I didn't take in much of what he said.'

Then it had got worse, I thought. Or perhaps the shock and disappointment of finding I was not there, at journey's end, would be enough to cause a temporary slipping back. I could hope this, at any rate. More and more, I felt that making Hong Kong had been a tremendous endeavour on Johnny's part, not the chance of the sea, washing him up in a far eastern port. Just as tracking down my new address on Aberdeen Bay must have been more than an inclination, now that he was no longer a hurt child, to let bygones be bygones and forgive me. Some stronger motive was required than the feeling, 'Might as well see her while I'm here, since I don't know anyone else in the place.'

'He was trying to tell me something about a dock-strike,' Barney said. 'Or a lock-out, was it? Giving him – something or other.'

'The chance of one trip out East, possibly? He's been on a South American cattle run, till quite recently. Has there been shipping trouble in South America in the last three months? You'd know that through export reports, wouldn't you? I've been out of touch with that sort of news.'

'Oh, yes. Complete hold-up in the docks at Buenos Aires. Lot of our stuff couldn't be unloaded. Several freighters we were interested in unable to sail for weeks. Simply held up in port – paying demurrage, of course, on our account. Any amount of trouble there's been – Some sort of head-on collision between the Government and the shipping companies.'

'Then that would have given him what he wanted, I think. Without breaking his contract with his regular employers, he could sign on for one voyage, out and back, with another company, couldn't he? If his own ship was prevented from sailing for any reason?'

'I suppose so. I'm afraid I didn't take to him, so I didn't pay much attention.

'He's not yet eighteen,' I said. 'I've no doubt he's been lying about his age to get jobs in foreign lines, probably under-paid jobs older men wouldn't take – wouldn't be offered. On a card he sent me he called himself a hand in a cattle boat. I think that was just making himself big: more likely he's a galley-boy, in the sort of grim, slow little ships where the owners aren't too fussy about regulations, or the conditions of the crew. Cattle boats, salt fish carriers. Wallowing around, taking months to get anywhere. Don't you think it shows quite a bit of initiative, working his way out here, at his age? And now I expect he's on his way back to South America. Back to the cattle run.'

'Yes, I expect so. I'm sorry, if I'd known there was anything special about the lad, from your point of view, I'd have borne with that stammer a bit longer, and asked him some questions. But it was pretty trying.'

I clenched my fingers round my passport and ticket in order not to cry out, 'Your son and mine, if he'd lived, would have looked like that boy. Very much like that boy, in whom you couldn't be interested. And I hope he'd have had the courage of that boy, tackling the world alone, handicapped in a way our son wouldn't have been. Indeed, I hope so!' Instead I told him, not very graciously, 'You couldn't be expected to know he was a favourite patient. I see that. What's done's done, and he's gone,' and we changed the subject. Presently, as usual, I felt apologetic, and tried to show it by being more appreciative of the trouble Barney had taken in getting up before dawn to meet me.

He said, 'Chloe, it's grand, seeing you're so much better, at last. But if you honestly don't mind, I think it would be a good idea if I went off and had some breakfast now. This is one of my teaching evenings, which means a sandwich in the office after work, by way of dinner.'

'I'm fine,' I assured him. 'You go. You've only just got time.'

'Well, I will then. Apart from missing dinner I'll have to spend most of the lunch hour having a heart-to-heart talk with our new Head Clerk. He isn't shaping as well as I thought he would.'

'What's the matter?' I asked, avoiding Ah Lee's eye as he stood behind Barney, patiently waiting for Master to say that they could both go.

'Oh, always trying to put the blame for anything that goes wrong on to someone else, which is the sort of thing I will not have. Either he's got to take responsibility, when he is responsible, or someone else from the outer office will get promoted in his place. I'll do my best to get over to Macao to see you next weekend, or the one after. This just happens to be a busy patch. Come along, Ah Lee. Want you do quick shop for me. Missee go well.'

It was extraordinary, in Hong Kong, how easy it was for even the most intelligent people to fall into the habit of talking pigeon unnecessarily. I had marvelled at bankers, journalists, diplomatic people, doing it without, apparently, noticing the lapse. Half the ladies on the Peak never spoke anything else to Chinese servants, even when the servants talked excellent English in return. Barney, dealing all day with Chinese clerks, packers, and shippers, had given up the effort to avoid it. He caught my look and smiled back.

'Yes, awful, isn't it!' he said confidentially, and we parted affably enough.

But he did not come to Macao. I did not mind. By the next weekend I was firmly in tow to that formidable woman, Honuong's grandmother's Third Cousin, the family prostitute, over whom there had been so many tears, long ago.

CHAPTER XIII

Interlude in Macao

THE CLAMMY WHITE blanket of fog remained wrapped round the ferry till we were within an hour's run of Macao. It was a discordant trip – the ear and the eye were aware of two wholly different worlds. This illness had made me extremely sensitive to noise and never, even in Hong Kong, had I heard so much, for so long, at such inescapably close quarters.

Three sets of passengers had brought on deck with them the portable transistor radios, regrettably cheap and powerful, with which Japan had just begun to flood the noise-hungry market of the Far East. Two were tuned in to one local station, which relayed American jazz, and the third to Hong Kong's alternative channel, giving out music on the Chinese scale. All were turned up to full volume, to drown competition, at least within the radius of a few yards. There was also a good deal of shouting going on, men, women, and children mingling their voices.

I made my way round the deck, to see who could bear this racket from near by, and what the shouting was about. I found one Chinese youth asleep in a chair alongside his machine, the lone upholder of Oriental music. By another transistor, two Eurasian boys had their heads bent sideways, almost touching the grid, to savour the amplification of the foreign dance band. The third radio was playing in the midst of a large, merry Cantonese family party, with the owners giving it no attention, except for yelling their conversation at one another instead of talking: there was more 'ho-ho-ing' going on than usual: so many words were lost in the din.

But outside our small craft was a blind, mysterious world, hueless and primeval: the swirling vapour our bows thrust aside was the low cloud which brooded over the face of the waters when earth took shape. From time to time rents appeared in it, to show us the rocky sides, but not the tops, of islands which floated past us. The tops were unimaginable territory, concealed behind a pale radiance which grew and grew, as the sun began to force its way through. It would have been a deeply impressive scene, had the specialist failed and I gone deaf. Sound reduced its dignity to the level of 'Yew . . . trew . . . love . . . moon up above,' yowled against the wailing of Chinese quarter-tones.

Then a head-wind sprang up, rolling the mist aft, swiftly bundling up the last wisps into a barrier which hung behind us, suspended between sea and sky, cutting us off from everything we had known, and ahead all was glory, the sun blazing on the bluest water. Even the transistors could not spoil this last half hour of the journey.

A fleet of fishing junks were making towards the Portuguese harbour, too, and we chugged through them; their sails were more tattered and patched with unexpected colours than similar craft in Hong Kong. From a distance their high sterns looked proud and, to western eyes, Elizabethan, but always, from near to, when we drew level with them and could look down, into the part where the family lived, they were beautifully domestic in a Chinese way. Some woman in a sampan-hat was washing a baby in a cooking pot. A small boy, wearing nothing but his hat, looked like a happy living mushroom. Someone else brought a brazier up from the hold and set it on deck for the new breeze to fan. ('The here and now, old Clo! Forget everything but the here and now. They are turning rich again.')

From the Red shore, Macao being a tiny promontory surrounded on all sides by China, a gunboat put out and took station alongside the ferry, near enough for us to see clearly the Communist flag. A machine-gun, looking very business-like, was mounted on the fore-deck and trained across our bows. At once, from Portuguese water, another gunboat, under the flag of the Colony, took up station on our other side. Her weapon was trained on the Communist craft. For a few minutes, with the creep of physical fear on the back of my neck, I thought we were about to be in the cross-fire of a battle, but the radios went on playing, nobody else took any notice, and I concluded it was the usual procedure. Both gunboats escorted us as far as the harbour, where one shore was Communist and the other Colonial, and then they turned away, at the same moment.

I stepped ashore into a dilapidated pocket of Europe and the pleasant persuasion, which grew to certainty within a few hours, that if I had to kill time anywhere before returning to Hong Kong, this was the right place in which to do just that. To think intelligently, or work, or try anything constructive in Macao would be appallingly difficult. It must be one of the laziest spots on earth. But I found it utterly charming, in a gentle, decorative way. The bustling East had disappeared: here was the West, in advanced decay.

The taxi which took me from the quay to the hotel, where the furniture was heavily Victorian and the view superb, wheezed and boiled as if it would never manage the steep, cobbled slope; but it won, and I felt half inclined to congratulate the driver, as well as tip him.

When I strolled round the town after tea, nearly everything I saw looked to be falling down, or to have fallen down, some time during the last four hundred years, the period of the Portuguese occupation, and no-one had bothered to clear away the rubble. Green and black lichen grew over crumbling white walls round a convent whose bells startled me: here, there seemed little point in shutting oneself away from the world when the world was so far off, anyway. Chinese faces in the street gave me what I had hankered for in Japan, the sense that around me were people whose company I could enjoy, if I came to know them. Even so, the majority of them were at least part-European: a race apart, the Macinese had been produced by generations of inter-breeding between the Portuguese settlers and their colonists. So far as I could judge, these people had kept the Chinese zest and turned it to the enjoyment of doing absolutely nothing, or at best, very little. The atmosphere was one of perpetual Sunday afternoon. Though the place was manifestly poverty-stricken, few of the inhabitants seemed inclined to make any strenuous efforts towards bettering their condition. The contrast with Hong Kong was strong everywhere, strongest in the behaviour of shop-keepers. Having left my fountain pen in Japan, I went into a small shop to buy, if possible, a cheap substitute in order dutifully to inform Barney of my safe arrival. The proprietor looked up with a bland smile from his evening rice-bowl, steaming on the counter, and told me that he was closed. Just down the road, however, was his brother's shop which, he said, would be open at this hour. He was mistaken.

The convent bells disturbed my sleep a little that first night – I was never conscious of them thereafter as an interruption of anything, only as a sweet, sad background, easy to ignore if I wished to ignore it – and I got up and went out on to the balcony on which the long windows of my room opened, to watch the lights of the fishing fleet weaving slow patterns on the glimmering sea, and to let my thoughts wander. I would make a practise of doing this, I promised myself, whenever I happened to wake during the dark hours, and for a matter of minutes only, I would allow memories of interested eyes, laughter, a kiss – anything deliberately shut out of my daylight mind – to mix with fantasies of a wholly different life, knowing all the while that my thoughts, like good little sheep, could be safely penned again when morning came.

The next day a fat, elderly Chinese woman waddled up to me as I was looking at the façade of the sixteenth century Christian church. She stood sideways to me, shooting glances from downcast eyes, too diffident to speak at first: there was that flickering of the lids I had noticed in Honuong and her relations when they were nervous. I went on examining the vast front wall with its noble traceries. There was not even a ruin behind it, nothing but the façade remained, standing at the top of a mighty flight of steps, with rough open ground beyond, where the body of the church should have been. 'You wondering what 'appened to the rest of it,' she said in a mournful tone, with a strong Yorkshire accent. 'Burnt oop, they do say. Years ago. 'Ad your breakfast.'

'Have I – ?' For a second I took this as a question, not a statement. 'Well, yes. Thank you.' One of my sheep leapt unbidden out of its pen, and needed to be chivvied back: the particular ring of a voice explaining: 'I said, "You've eaten your morning rice, and are cutting wood".'

'You Mrs. Freeborn.' Again this was a statement, not a question. Her sad manner made it almost an accusation.

'That's right. How do you know?' A silly query in this part of the world.

'Friend of a friend of mine, friend of Ah Lee. Watch you get on the ferry.'

'Oh. I see.'

'You been good to my family,' she said, as though this were something to deplore, and then her voice turned peevish, 'though why you not let Honuong come work for me, I don't know!'

'Honuong,' I said, realizing who this must be, 'is going to do very well for herself, on her own.'

'She do it quicker with me. I say one thing for these Macinese – no good any other way – they free with money when they got any. I know. I married one. Croupier in a fan-tan house. Deserving fellow.'

Nonplussed by the last words, I said, 'Oh, yes, I'm sure he is,' for want of anything else to say. It was some time later in our acquaintanceship that I found 'deserving' meant, to Third Cousin, anyone who had not yet got his deserts. In her world, these were generally bad. It was an ambiguous word, anyway, and I accepted that her use of it was as reasonable as mine.

'Free with his money to everyone but me!'

She shook with laughter. One should always laugh, by Chinese good manners, when imparting regrettable news, lest the hearer become depressed – another of my thought-sheep needed re-penning: Tom Jarvis had told me this, while we watched the sampan girls taking over Lory's ship.

Sweat ran down the creases of Third Cousin's large gloomy face. 'He marry to get free cook, I luv, no good for cooking! You would not like to come to my 'ouse for tea.'

'Oh, but I should,' I said, falling into the small social trap,

196

with only a passing reflection that there was nothing Barney would like less, if he came to Macao to see me, than to find me on visiting terms with the local ex-whore, or one of them. But Barney, something told me, would not be coming.

'It must be poor meal. Maybe, terrible.' In her moods of self-deprecation, Third Cousin's wording, as well as her intonation, lost the sturdy Midland ring and became far more Chinese.

'Oh, I shouldn't want anything but a cup of tea. One afternoon perhaps. I'm likely to be here some weeks.'

'Why not now? Mr. Cartwright liked 'is morning tea, and I've sort of kept the 'abit.'

'Oh. Well. All right.' Too late, I recalled that I was not supposed to go where germs congregated, and it was more than probable that the house where I was being invited was something like the tenement in Kowloon. But Third Cousin was fascinating in her swift alternations between abasement and aggression. I was not going to be put off seeing her at home by last-minute caution. 'For love of knowing what should not be known – ' Either one is born with devouring curiosity about other human beings, or one is not. It must save a great deal of trouble if one is not.

We walked towards the harbour. 'Mr. Cartwright,' I said. 'That's your husband? The croupier? I've never seen fan-tan played, but of course I've heard of it.'

'Well, if you ask me, it's one bloody silly game. You can't beat the odds. But you're welcome to look where 'e works. 'E'll tell you the way luck's running, if is running. And 'e not too far gone with chasing the dragon's tail. Smoke, you know. Not that 'e does it when working – Yet. Delgado, that's our name. Mr. Cartwright, now, was different – '

But he, too, was a deserving fellow. From Bradford. Third Cousin had no means of knowing whether or not his deserts had caught up with him, at last. For two years, before the war, he had kept her, off and on, while he travelled in chemists' supplies through the Far East. His job sounded to me so much like Mr. Kenderdine's that I wondered if Mrs. Kenderdine, encompassing her husband's path with imaginary dangers, really had other risks to fear which she preferred to turn into physical terrors in her mind. Mr. Cartwright had plainly been the one stable element in Third Cousin's chaotic life, and he had failed her in the end, like everything and everyone else. Slowing my steps to hers, down the tree shaded quay, along an arcaded street, with the intermittent Yorkshire echo in my ears, I found the European impression of Macao overwhelming.

Now that I had got friendly with her, Third Cousin said, switching over to her pushing mood, I must write to Honuong and say she would do well to come.

'No.'

'Why not?'

'Why should I?'

'Woman I know, back in Hong Kong, she says the mother would like it.'

'Possibly. But that doesn't seem to me a good reason.' Unfortunately, for any young Chinese, I thought, family pressure would seem the best possible reason for doing anything: if Honuong failed in her ambition, this was where she would probably end up, helping Third Cousin twice removed, in spite of her independent spirit.

'Oh well, 'ere we are.'

A two-roomed, ground-floor flat, the Delgado home was like the tenement only in being overcrowded, but not with human-beings: here there was an excess of furniture. It was crammed with unsuitably stuffy arm-chairs, pouffes, lamps with bobbled shades, knick-knacks of all kinds, innumerable home-from-home bits which Mr. Cartwright had collected in his wanderings, and left behind when he walked out. There was a strong smell of dust, long undisturbed.

She pointed out the last thing he gave her, a poker-work

motto, still hanging over the door into the bedroom: 'Today is the Tomorrow you worried about Yesterday.'

' 'E told me that means, "Don't worry." Bloody well I should a worried! 'E said, "Back in six weeks as usual," and that was twelve years ago. You think there's too much furniture? Sometimes 'e said, "Mei, we're too cluttered oop for the summer." But they're nice rooms. Get the sea-breeze. Aren't they nice rooms? You don't think so? Oh, well.'

'They certainly are. Very nice. Lovely to get the breeze, in this heat.' In fact, little of it came through so much impediment of grey lace curtains, and then looped, heavier curtains, and all that woodwork and leatherwork and upholstery.

In the next room, with the door open between us, her husband was asleep or unconscious on a mat. He had the same hollow look as the ex-porter on our roof, but Delgado was younger and not yet so wasted by the drug. 'It's not 'is working night,' Third Cousin observed and took no further notice of him.

I found something else complimentary to say about the rooms: they faced the harbour and the junks at rest there were a splendid sight with their nets drying from the mastheads and swirling out on the breeze. She rounded on me triumphantly: 'That's right. That's why I wanted you to see where I live. So you tell Honuong –'

'No!'

'Oh, well. I get tea.'

This was hard to swallow – mixed for my benefit, before I could prevent it, with a quantity of condensed milk. The sticky home-made sweet-meat I was implored to taste was repulsive to someone with no liking for sweet things anyway, and I put it down half eaten.

'You see. I am bad cook. Like I said.' Submission and resignation was in every line of her melancholy bulk.

This time I was not to be drawn into gainsaying anything. I claimed to be rarely hungry in the middle of the morning:

had I not said I should only want a cup of tea? Harking back to my trip from Hong Kong I asked about the gunboats. Were they always there, on either side of the ferry coming into the harbour?

So people said. And on the way out, too. Third Cousin herself had not left Macao for over twenty years.

'But what are they there for, d'you think?'

'Oh, don' know, luv. One cooms because the other cooms.' This seemed to her neither interesting nor remarkable.

'But what do the crews think they're doing?'

'Don't suppose they know, either. You want some stamps? Very pretty stamps, Macao 'as. Everyone says that. You take away stamps of all value, can sell them or make a good present!'

'I don't know anyone who collects stamps,' I said. 'Someone in authority must have sent the gunboats out in the first place. For some purpose.'

'Daresay. Maybe on a birthday. Salazar's or Chou en Lai's. One Communist boat for show. So then another boat, for show. Portuguese.'

'And then those in authority simply forgot?'

'I let you have stamps cheap. Very pretty. Whole set. Many not now printed. More valuable like that.' Some client, in the old days, must have gypped her with an odd payment.

'No stamps. Tell me, what part of China did your family come from?'

'They didn't say. You think they come over illegal?' The eyes flickered. There was some strange loyalty here, still, to those who had made an outcast of her.

'Of course I know they came over that way. But I'm not wanting to have them sent back. I'm just interested in the length of the journey they made. Because I fancy they came from somewhere towards the middle of China. Some district where they weave the design of the cloud, the bird, and the moon. Does that mean anything to you?'

'Oh, I 'ad a cheongsam like that! My first. They give it me to go away in – ' The flabby features quivered. For a horrified moment I thought that, hit suddenly by the recollection, she was going to cry. Tears coursing down those creases would seem unbearably moving and unsuitable. But she recovered and said, gasping, 'So long ago! Not thought of it in years!' and then repeated, almost word for word, what Honuong had said. 'I dunno where we come from, that's a fact! We called it, "our village." Must a got a name, but we just said, "our village." They took me so young to Shanghai.'

As a little girl she would not have worn a cheongsam, the woman's garment, but she had been turned viciously into a woman at fifteen. She gave me small, terrible details of what it had been like in her early days in Shanghai; hints coming through clumsy words of a child's fear and loneliness and despair, knowing that she could never go back to her family. But in the end fear and despair had given way – and it was as well that they should – to indifference, and her present rapacity.

It was while she was talking of the Shanghai brothel that I noticed something which had not struck me before: she had no gold teeth: only gaps and a few of her own. For her, there had been no good lovers, except Mr. Cartwright, and he had left her furniture, not gold caps. Still, furniture was better than nothing: it gave prestige, too. I surmised that she was wrong in thinking that she had been married, surprisingly late in life, in order that she should cook for the croupier: it was much more likely to have been for her chairs and lamps and curtains.

She dried her nose on her sleeve and asked after the health of the grandmother, her companion in childhood. Curiosity was ambivalent here: it was nice to be told that so far as I knew, not having seen the old woman for months, she was well: it was nicer still to make sure that she, the fortunate one in the old days, the girl who stayed sheltered at home, was now worse off materially than luckless, shunned Third

Cousin. Was it possible, no furniture worth mentioning? She asked me twice: really, no chairs? No rugs? Not even a motto, I said comfortingly.

She brisked up, though her voice still kept the dying fall which had become habitual.

'When you write to Honuong – ' She pronounced the name Shanghai-fashion, so that it lost its prettiness and became 'onion.' It seemed to me to be symbolical of what would happen to Honuong if she ever came here.

'Get this clear. You have our relationship wrong. I'm not in charge of the girl.'

'She'd do what you say.'

'I doubt it. And anyway, I'm not saying she should come. I've never written to her. I don't suppose I ever shall. Unless I have to send her whatever testimonial she needs to become an air hostess. That's what she wants to be. "Heavenly shop-girl" to her. And that's what she'll become.'

'Sounds daft to me. There's money around in Macao, you know, when the tourists are in.'

'So I understand,' I said, thinking, 'I've had enough of this.' We had come full circle again. I got up. 'Before I go, thank you very much for the tea – '

'It was not nice. Could see you didn't enjoy it. You're used to better things.'

'Well, thank you very much, anyway.' Indeed it was time I got away: the smell of dust was becoming more and more pungent at the back of my nose.

I turned at the door. 'Just tell me this, because it's puzzling – I know that in the ordinary way everyone seems to know everything about everyone else around here, but if there's still no contact between you and Honuong's family, how do you, personally, get so much news of them? How did you hear it was my roof they were on, and her mother who thinks it would be a good thing for her to join you? – and be cut off, too?'

The two twittering aunt-like creatures were responsible, I learnt. I had forgotten them, they had appeared so briefly as part of the growing menage, at the beginning of our invasion. They were not related to the others, Third Cousin told me, being connected only with a business associate of Honuong's father. For them there was no bar of custom. Coming over to Macao to work in a fish-packing joint, they had sought her out at once.

'We'll go and see them round sundown tomorrow. Just before they knock oop. You'll like the fish-drying – '

'No, I really don't think – '

'And after that, he'll be all right and working – ' She jerked her head back towards the room where her husband sprawled. ' – So we'll all four take you to watch fan-tan in the evening.'

To my amazement I heard myself agreeing to this programme and arranging a time when I would come and pick her up at her home. I knew perfectly well that she would start all over again tiresomely trying to sell me a set of stamps, going on and on about Honuong. Sad and submissive-looking, she had the soft persistence of the drip of water torture. I told myself, on my way back alone to the hotel, that I had given in without more fight because of the aunt-like couple. I should like to have a talk with them while Third Cousin was handy to interpret. They might be able to explain something Third Cousin was unlikely to know after her long separation from the family: Honuong's unusual relationship with her parents. Why did she despise her father, and was this connected with the mother's readiness to get rid of her, to deliver her into the hands of Third Cousin?

But the real reason was different, and by the time I reached my room I knew it. Actually, I wanted to see Third Cousin again: she reminded me irresistibly of something I had been very fond of in England: our old cat, the one who used to watch the swallows, hour after hour, day after day, always thinking she was going to catch one. They shared the same disarming, almost lunatic ability to hope, disregarding experience.

There was something gruesomely magnificent about a woman who had come, persistent and undiscouraged, through the miserable sort of life Third Cousin had endured.

I wrote that night to Laura Cairns, addressing the letter to the Peninsula Hotel, Kowloon, marked 'To Await Arrival.' As Barney and I had agreed, she had a kind heart. I asked her urgently to let me know exactly what the procedure should be for a Chinese girl to get herself taken on as one of B.O.A.C.'s local air hostesses.

I should have done this before, I thought, and not waited to get the know-how for her till I met that bulldog figure, Third Cousin. Feeling slightly depressed, as I had done, because Honuong did not appear to need me any longer, had been stupid irresponsibility on my part – self-pitying irresponsibility, the worst kind. Whether she herself thought so, or not, Honuong needed help still to keep out of Macao, and all it would entail for her. On second thoughts, Third Cousin was not a bulldog: the wrong simile had been suggested by her bulk: she was a spider, equally tenacious and more merciless, size for size: and, moreover, a spider which knew what prey it wanted. For myself, I was well-disposed towards the spider, could not help liking its gusto: but not in connection with any fly in which I took an interest.

The next day was full of everything the doctor had warned me to avoid: insanitary surroundings, over-breathed air undoubtedly laden with the widest variety of active infection, and hours of close proximity to far too many people. All the same, telling myself that none of these things mattered just for one day, I was glad I had not been adamant with Third Cousin when she suggested visiting the fish-curing twitterers. I saw, for the first and last time, the other side of Macao's genial existence.

Here in essence, behind the scenes, was a pre-Industrial

Revolution state. Not even in theory were there any regulations to protect labour from the greed of too-few employers. In the fish-packing station, hours were long; as long, I gathered, as workers could be induced to stand when they had no alternative open to them; and wages were grimly low. Conditions would have made an English shop-steward faint. At least in Hong Kong there were always new projects starting, promising hope, or the possibility of change, the substitute for hope: but not in Macao.

When a fishing junk's catch was bought for export, it was sun-cured in the open air, which meant that at a certain stage it went putrid, before the heat destroyed the germs again. The two middle-aged women, who recognized me from our one roof-meeting and chirped politely in unison, must have been much stronger than they looked: they worked roughly from sunrise to sunset among the trays of fish half-way through the process. However, they seemed very thankful indeed to have found a niche at all, even though the work was seasonal and would stop with the end of the bright weather. They had no complaints.

As informants they were disappointing. Their idea of answering a question was to repeat it as a fact, or so it appeared through Third Cousin's translation. Conversation ran, 'Ask them, if you would, if they can explain why Honuong is so bitter about her father? This must be most unusual in a Chinese girl.' – 'Yes, they say, most unusual in Chinese girl.' – 'Then why?' – 'Because Honuong don't like 'er father.' And, 'Does the mother resent that? Is she angry because the girl talks of him without respect?' – 'The mother is angry when girls talks without respect.' – 'Could that be why the mother is willing for Honuong to leave the family for ever, by coming to work for you?' – 'They say, is just because she – the mother – agrees girl should so leave her family.' – 'You see?' Third Cousin put in, speaking on her own behalf. 'She agrees all right. If you was to send a letter – '

A possibility which occurred to me was that the answers were more enlightening in Cantonese than in English, and the intermediary could not be bothered to render more fully an exchange which would sell no stamps for her, and get her no professional help. My Cantonese had slipped back a little in Japan: I thought I detected one or two interesting words in the twitter which did not feature in the rendering I was given, but I could not be sure. I never learnt what strains in human relationships had produced these surprising family hatreds. Third Cousin spoke of her own father only once in my hearing, and then with wistful pride. He was a good man who had fallen on evil days: what he had done was what was required of him. There was nothing else for him to do. She said, as though this were one of the major hardships of her life, 'Didn't know for more'n a year when 'e died.'

Never, even among the Chinese, had I met such a resilient spirit. In four hours I counted five attempts to get a commission out of me somehow: the most pressing was now that I should order some shoes through a friend of hers, an old client who would make them to measure wonderfully well and wonderfully cheaply; and every fresh effort, like the cat's mews towards the nests, spoke of hope unflecked by any memory of previous failure.

On the way to one of the fan-tan houses, with the other two women walking behind, we went a long detour against my will and probably theirs – they had worked standing for nearly twelve hours – in order that I should see the outside of the shop where the remarkable shoe-maker lived. Fortunately it was closed. With three dusty pairs of vast slippers in the window, nestling against jars of sweets and dummy cigarette-cartons, bleached by sun and time, it was not an inviting looking place. 'Oh, well, you can order them by yourself tomorrow,' she said. 'Now you know where to come. If you say I sent you, my friend will make a special price for you.' Of this I had no doubt, and she was right, too, in what she had said about fan-tan. It was the dullest form of gambling I had ever tried, and as the evening wore on it became more and more incredible to me that the Macinese remained its devotees, men, women, and children alike.

We spent half an hour or so in two other fan-tan houses, to see how luck was running that evening, before settling down in the establishment where the resuscitated croupier-husband brooded over a table. He was a handsome fellow, in a cadaverous way, in his better moments looking with his long black moustaches like an early portrait of Robert Louis Stevenson, and he was certainly, I thought, not more than half his wife's age. Stronger grew the pitying conviction that he had married her, not for her cooking but for Mr. Cartwright's furniture, which could be sold, for more smoke, in the final stages, when the worst came to the worst and he lost his job. 'All right,' I said rashly, in one of the long intervals in the betting, when no-one seemed to want to put anything on any number, 'I'll order a pair of shoes! But not just yet, mind you. Before I go,' and it was as if I had given a sweet to a child. Here dropped some little piece of manna Third Cousin would be able to hide away, without his knowing of it, the deserving rat.

Seeing our party of four come in, he sent along a message to his wife that nothing seemed to be coming up specially. In the other two houses luck had been indecisive, too. Sometimes, I was told, there were '2' evenings, or '3' evenings, but this was not one of them.

The houses were all exactly alike: with hard chairs and spittoons as the only equipment except the gaming-tables: and no effort whatever towards glamour or comfort anywhere. The players sat in a gallery and let down their bets in small baskets on strings, to the table in a big room below where the croupier had a pile of ordinary shirt-buttons in front of him. From time to time he inverted a tin cup over the pile, separated a number of buttons from the rest by moving the cup along the table, and accepted wagers as to how many buttons would be left over when he had sorted those which had been under the cup into fours, with a ruler. One, two, three, or none. No cheating was possible. Third Cousin repeated to me with contemptuous satisfaction in case I had forgotten this, that the odds were always three to one against the player, and no successful system had ever been devised to combat them. 'Bloody silly, Mr. Cartwright said, and it's the truest thing 'e ever did say, if you ast me.'

One or two off-season tourists like myself were playing, but most of those present were only watching. The real addicts came every night, and usually lost the small amount of cash they could spare early in the evening: but while anyone was in the gallery who might play, the fan-tan houses stayed open, and the staff went on with the same procedure, all through the night if need be; and while anyone would play, the watchers remained there, fascinated.

At the end of two and a half hours, I had won about half a crown and lost about three and tenpence. I had put a few bets on for Third Cousin and the two twitterers. She was up nine-pence: I paid the loss of five shillings; and the others had won nothing on three stakes of two shillings each. The best that could be said for this form of entertainment was that it was cheap, considering the time consumed.

The pleasantest sight were the coolie women who came in from the fields round the town with their babies, fast asleep, strapped on their backs, to stare in wonder at the spectacle of small sums of money changing hands with no-one doing anything to earn them.

Eventually, bored beyond further endurance, I left ten shillings to be gambled away as the three women pleased, and escaped into the soft, luminous night. Even my capacity to enjoy anything once had been exhausted, temporarily, and I knew that nothing would ever lure me again into the dreary dissipation of a fan-tan house. Still, I was pleased to have seen it – and, whether I deserved this or not – suffered no medical ill-effect from that staidest of debauches. No-one had tried to sell us a drink throughout the evening, though Macao, with Portuguese wine to be bought in practically every post-card shop, was far from dry: but vice, like everything else around the place, was under-organized: it was part of the charm.

I walked very fast back to the hotel, through the gloom of the subtly European streets, where darkness seemed more dangerous than in the poorest quarters of Kowloon because of the hybrid character: but the loafing shadows by the few lamp-posts remained shadows, and I went into the hotel looking forward to a late snack and, less prosaically, to a few moments on the balcony for the loosing of fancy.

My husband's writing on an envelope lying on the hall table alarmed me, and disinterested me in the idea of supper. I had a packet of biscuits in my room and that, I thought, would do for tonight – Barney and I wrote to one another, with some difficulty, once a week, on Sundays, while I was away ill. A mid-week letter like this boded no good, and I took it upstairs to read in solitude. But the news in it turned out to be innocuous enough, from my point of view, except for one sentence towards the end.

The first part of the letter merely proved that I had indeed put off writing on Honuong's behalf for too long: Barney mentioned that Laura had been switched to another route and would not be coming back to Hong Kong. I could picture her, like a nun in her vocation, obediently and unquestioningly dropping all contacts in one place, to take up others without a backward glance. Eventually, no doubt, my letter to the Peninsula Hotel would catch up with her, somewhere on the Stockholm–Oslo–London run. But knowing Laura and her ability to shrug off the past, I could not imagine her bothering to answer, kind heart or no kind heart, a missive only connected with the Far East Service which she had left behind. She would intend to, and forget, with the same ease with which she forgot lovers.

The rest of the letter was given to working out in detail the pros and cons of his coming to Macao, not the next weekend, nor the one after that – both, unfortunately, impossible for unspecified reasons – but the third from the time of writing. This was the purpose of the letter: to let me know that he would have to see, nearer the time. But on the whole, he felt, the absence of senior staff on Saturday morning, when it could be avoided, was undesirable soon after a number of the junior staff had required pulling up for sloppy time-keeping. That was the casual reference to further trouble in the office which sent cold into my mind.

Never, I thought irritably, could there have been a man with a firmer grasp of inessentials; and then realised that here, once more, was my particular weakness showing itself. Barney was a better human being than I was, and I could not get over my petty resentment of it. I went to sleep vaguely troubled, and had two indulgent balcony sessions that night, observing the moving points of light out in the bay. Whichever way I looked, the menacing dark hills of China bounded the view, and after a while the much more important threat of the great, sprawling mass of hostile territory all round, soothed my own personal worries, much as the presence of desperate people on my roof had done.

In the morning, after an enormous breakfast, I fell in love all over again with Macao, after the slight dimming of my affection in the squalor of the fish-packing station and the inadequate gambling dens.

Sunday afternoon reigned again, though in fact it was Thursday. On rickety platforms built out from the quay, seine-fishers wound up and down their spidery nets, looking content, catching nothing, even more part of the European scene than the old merchant-adventurers' graves, English and Portuguese, which I found in the neglected cemetery. 'Here lyeth ... gentleman ... from Bristol ... 1683.'

Several uniformed African soldiers, brought in bewilderment from Portuguese East, lounged about in various stages of unbuttonment, guarding the ancient fort on the hill above the town, presumably from the six hundred millions of Red Chinese on the other side of the harbour. I knew that repeatedly, when the tiny existence of Macao was remembered, China asked Portugal to relinquish her two-mile-wide strip of territory, and repeatedly, Portugal refused. On the last occasion, just before I arrived, the Chinese Premier, Chou en Lai, had described this as 'The case of a small nation bullying a big one.' And these were the bullies, not even smart, urban Bantu types, but primitive-looking black men from a particularly backward part of Africa. Everything seemed refreshingly unreal – perhaps Barney was not doing as badly in the office as I feared.

I took comfort from the international situation, as I had during the night. If the Communists, were they so inclined, could take Hong Kong in one violent day, there was obviously no need for them to use force at all to get Macao: the upper reaches of the boundary river, the only water supply of the Colony, came meandering down through Red China: the flow could be damned and diverted. But luckily it was possible to be either so rich or so poor as to be virtually safe in the fear-ridden modern world: if Hong Kong had become so wealthy as a free port that China found it an invaluable trading-post with the West, Macao was now so poor that taking it ruthlessly could not be worth, except as a matter of 'face,' the fuss it would certainly cause among other nations: even in China 'face' could be bought at too high a price. So the solemn, thick-lipped, unmilitary figures of the Portuguese native troops remained desultorily at their posts round the seventeenth century walls, ready to defend to the death, or near, something whose importance had not been explained to them, for who could explain it?

In the hotel, a remarkably cosmopolitan little set collected in the bar before lunch and dinner, and they, too, helped to restore my confidence in the permanency of my world, as it was at the moment: they seemed so convinced of the lasting quality of their own.

A young-middle aged peasant from Kuwait engaged me in bad French. 'Madame, in my country – since the oil, you understand – life is wonderful. We are paid to send our children to school. Boys and girls. Imagine, girls too! If your child scores more than eighty per cent marks in the term you receive a bonus. If you have five clever children and a small piece of land you can retire and travel!'

'And you have five clever children, Monsieur?'

'I have six, Madame. Please to drink something for me. I am Muslim and admit no alcohol. But please to drink something quite expensive.' I chose a champagne cocktail and we both enjoyed it, the proxy-drinker possibly more than I did. It was made of a very sweet Portuguese substitute, but the price was just like the real thing.

Standing in the same group with us at the bar, so that we naturally fell into conversation, was a most unusual Chinese magnate from Singapore. Coming of an old and distinguished family, as he confided to me, he had a passion for Western culture. Wishing his daughter to bear an aristocratic English name he had called this languid creature, who did crossword puzzles in the lounge all day, Ivy.

An influx of tourists had crowded the hotel for one day. My table was shared, for two meals, by a minor Italian film actress, sulking in Macao in order to wring a concession from the company she worked for in Cairo, and a representative of the employers, an Egyptian, sent after her to persuade her to return to the half-finished production on location near Khartoum. Their *lingua franca* was Americanised English. Hearing me talk schoolgirl and war-time Brussels' French to the Kuwait oil-digger, they concluded that I would not understand this, and went on with their quarrel in my presence: or perhaps they did not care.

'Imagine! The lizards! And what they did! Never, never again, I say! For the first time in Egypt, I see a film of me projected in the open air. On a wall. White-washed. At night – '

'Is common practice in also the South of France,' repeated the representative wearily. 'Also in South America. Also through Middle East. Also, I think, it happens some places in Italy – '

'Never. Or I have not seen it. Or we have no such lizards, big, big! Ugh, those great lizards!'

'I tell you once, dear, I tell you twice. Now I tell you again – Maybe you understand three times? – The company cannot agree to put a clause in your contract, cutting out open air projection.'

'They will agree. Or else! Maybe they like to find some-one, not me, after all this time and all this shooting, to remake that picture? You think they like to waste all those dollars?'

'That's blackmail, dear, and you know it.'

'What I know is, how they run, those lizards! Imagine, you, the quickness of the lizards. Alerted by the light, by the moving of shadows, they run about the wall like mad things. Over my face, they run, in close-up! In a moment of how you call it, renunciation, one there goes, down my neck, into my bosom. In the front seats, the fools of audience, they begin to laugh. They begin to clap. When there should be tears.'

'Home run. Sure they clap,' said the young man. 'For the tenth time, dear, we don't control projection. We only make pictures! Can't you understand anything?'

'At the back, they may not see the lizard. But laughter, when it is stupid, is catching. And always more lizards come, because of the warmth on the wall. They like. I open my mouth for a kiss – '

'Try keeping it closed next time,' he said. 'It has been done that way.'

She threw him a sultry look, got up, flung her napkin on

the table, and walked out of the dining room. The napkin upset my modest bottle of Perrier – somehow I could not fancy the river water, having seen a few Chinese villages beside other streams – but my glass was immediately replenished with something far more costly by the father of so many clever, oil-born children.

At dinner the film pair were still fighting, but something must have happened during the night: they started back for Khartoum together, she all dimpled smiles, in the morning.

When the blow fell, I could not have been less prepared for its coming. It was as if I had never foreseen it at all.

In a light, amused mood, I picked up another letter from Barney and slipped it unopened into my handbag before I started out after breakfast towards my favourite perch on the harbour wall. From here I could watch, on one side of me, the lovely frolicking of the wind with the drying nets, and the landing by the last junks home of their night's haul: and on my other side, if I swivelled half round on the wall, I could see the burning off of sea-growths from the hulls of boats which had been pulled out of the water at high tide. The drifting smoke and the figures moving in and out of it were very decorative. I had panicked the last time, unnecessarily, over Barney's letter: I was not going to panic again. In a leisurely way I took this one out of its envelope.

Here was the news from London I – but not he – had been expecting for months. Headquarters had decided that his contract, shortly due for renewal, would be allowed to expire. He would be replaced, as Manager, early in the new year.

My heart sickened with pity for him. He seemed stunned by the blow, repeating to me, word for word, the official pride-saving phrases in the letter from Headquarters: 'Owing to reorganization of staff . . . regret . . . other arrangements have had to be made' – phrases which surely never saved anyone's pride. No specific reasons were given for his replacement. Simply, his existing contract, which would run out shortly.

was not to be renewed. Another man would be coming to Hong Kong as Manager, Far East, at the end of the year.

Barney mentioned that in the tailpiece of the firm's letter he had been offered another post, at the salary he had been getting before his promotion; but not in London; or not, as the writer put it vaguely, 'for the time being.' There was a vacancy for a second-in-command in the Belfast office. He did not say if he intended to accept this.

I found tears falling on his writing, blotching it. They were wholly for him, at the moment, not for myself. To hide, I climbed into one of the aged taxis, thankful that the decrepit engine would take a long time to wheeze up to the hotel: I should be able to control myself by then, and make arrangements for going to Barney at once, though he had not asked that. All I wanted was to get to him quickly, to be of some slight comfort, if I could, in this bitter humiliation.

We had started to come together during my illness; perhaps now we could draw closer still. Sympathy might disguise for him, a little, the shape of failure; I could stress something that would be easier for this man to accept than for most others in his position – there was no disgrace in not being able to get on with people whose standards were not his. Was this true? I was not sure, but at least I could put the situation that way. I must try to bolster up whatever was left of his self-esteem. And my health would stand Hong Kong now: it had got to, anyway. Within two hours I was away, in the day-ferry.

The flurry of settling up and packing and catching the boat left no time to warn Barney of my coming, nor could I let poor Third Cousin know that I was not going to order shoes through her after all. I was an unprofitable friend. As much as I could be sorry, at that moment, for anything but the hurt to Barney, I was sorry not to be able to say goodbye to her. She was a gallant old tough, who must once have been vulnerable: so pathetically vulnerable that it scarcely bore thinking of –

she had begun to tell me about her ghastly early experiences in Shanghai. I liked her.

The two gunboats escorted us out to sea, flying their different national flags and aiming their guns at one another, and for some reason the absurdity of their being in attendance on the Macao ferry swung my thoughts to what this disaster for Barney might mean to me personally. A taste for absurdity has its uses in the Far East. I had always had that, and Barney had not. I should miss Hong Kong, terribly, perhaps less for its beauties than for its oddities. That in itself was absurd, I saw. Having agonised over coming to this place, I did not want to leave it when I must.

I turned on myself, fiercely: there was no excuse for self-pity: no need either: I had people on my side. All people, everywhere. Curiosity about people was one of the few handholds of the soul that did not give way in the grip of time. Wherever I was, I should be all right in my fashion. 'Now Clo – ! Old Clo. If you had a god you should be on your knees, thanking him for just this interest in other human beings.'

It was Barney who had no defences within himself: ill-starred Barney, who had never been able to bend to the winds of circumstance. If lying would help him now I was prepared to take his part hotly, to maintain that the firm was in the wrong, the surplanting wholly unjustifiable. But of course it was not: a good Manager must be able to rub along with his underlings. Someone, or probably several contacts had reported back to London the frequent change of head clerk and interference with the time-hallowed customs of Eastern trade.

CHAPTER XIV

The Change

TWENTY-FOUR HOURS passed between the writing of Barney's crushed letter, and my arrival at the new flat in Aberdeen: in this time his mood had swung from dejection to an extraordinary heartiness.

My presence was not required as comfort. I had the curious impression that he kept glancing about to see that nothing had been left around which should not be there. I told myself that this ebullience was the reaction of extreme disturbance; depression would return, but it did not. I could not make up my mind whether to be glad or sorry on his behalf that his attitude towards what had happened to him was one of pointless aggressiveness, something I had never seen in him before. He talked a good deal of forcing the firm to put on paper exactly what Headquarters had against him. Who had reported adversely? What had been alleged? I did what I could to dissuade him from this, saying, what was the use? There could be no legal redress for wrongful dismissal: a lawyer, consulted by Barney in the first shock of anger, while I was still in Macao, had affirmed that. A newly-appointed Manager was on probation for eighteen months, by the terms of a contract containing several of those small saving clauses often overlooked because no-one expects them to matter. In any case, the firm had offered him alternative employment. I was afraid, for him, of further explanations of why he had been found wanting. Mercifully, the Board was not to be drawn: the Secretary fell back on yet more non-committal phrases about policy and the employment of technical specialists in the field. What could he have written, in honesty, except, 'You are a man in a thousand, scrupulous, able, and energetic. But you cannot see into other men's minds, and, against this, the rest is unimportant'?

'You come back too late, Missee!' Ah Lee said mournfully, still unable to accept that I could have done nothing to avert calamity.

Barney staggered me, the day after my return, by ending some inattentive question about Macao with, ' – before you got tired of it,' as though this had been the reason for my return. Officially, between us, it became the reason for my return.

'Will you consider the Belfast job?' I asked.

'Heavens, no. What do you take me for? This firm's had eight years of my life. And in turn, I've "had" this firm, I can tell you! No, we'll go back to London, when I've handed over to my successor. And I may say I'll do that slightly more punctiliously than I should have done if they'd treated me decently! They'll have no cause for complaint. As a matter of fact, after more than a year's pretty useful experience out here, I ought to pick up something reasonable in the city without any difficulty at all.'

'I see,' I said. I suppose the instinct towards compassion and protection, in a woman without children, is not weakened but generalised, going out towards anything that is hurt. But I knew him so little, in this new, euphoric personality, that I could not think what to do to lessen the hurt, except to follow his lead. I could not even tell if he believed himself when he talked in this way. Could he possibly imagine that at forty it would ever be easy to start again, in some other line?

'I daresay, Chloe, you'll be quite pleased to take up your own work again?'

I could only say, yes. I would think about it as soon as I knew where we were going to live. Was it possible, once more, that in the self-centredness of a dreadful disappointment, he did not realise it would take years to build up a private practice again? That having given up Public Health

218

appointments to come out East, I could hardly expect those who had filled them for over a year to step aside for me because I came back. I wanted to cry again, because of what had been done to him, the blunting of whatever susceptibilities he had. His reactions, I thought unwillingly, were somewhat like Third Cousin's.

He turned practical: furniture for the new flat was not worth buying when we should need it for so short a time, not more than three months at the outside: we could hire what we needed. Because meanwhile, he said with gruesome light-heartedness, we ought to take full advantage of having a wonderful cook and adequate service at our disposal: we might never get that again, in England.

In the next few weeks we entertained far more than we had ever done before. In Kowloon we had spent little more then half the goodwill allowance Barney was given: anyone else would have saved it at this point, putting aside every possible Hong Kong dollar for the uncertain future; but to him this would be unthinkable. An expense account was provided for entertaining: he would use it all on creating goodwill for the firm in Hong Kong, or leave the residue behind. There were dinner parties for Ah Lee and his friends to serve, once or twice or three times a week, and corresponding meals out for Barney and me to eat, by way of returned hospitality.

In my nursery, when I was a small child, hung a highly imaginative picture: 'The Duchess of Richmond's Ball on the Eve of the Battle of Waterloo': I had not thought of it for many years: it kept returning to my mind's eye in this queer period. I recalled the young men as looking dashingly gay and debonair. Had they been, in fact, uneasy and frightened inside, longing for the time of waiting to be over?

It crossed my bewildered thoughts that Barney might be hoping to be offered another job of some kind in Hong Kong, by showing himself hail-fellow-well-met with everyone, giving the lie to rumours about his removal. Making a united front, in public, when he announced our return to England, he and I gave the impression, as best we could, that it was quite a normal thing, in his firm, for a Manager to be recalled after a year or so: after all, the Hong Kong office was not Headquarters – who knew what this shift might portend? But when I asked Barney in one of our rare private moments, if he would like to stay out East should an opportunity come his way, he said no to this, too, emphatically.

He kept up his teaching of mathematics, two evenings a week, having perforce dropped the third in the new press of engagements. But nothing was allowed to interfere with the two classes he kept. He was delighted, out of all proportion to the little triumph, when he finally succeeded in beguiling Mrs. Kenderdine into some voluntary good works. Under his renewed pressure she tried her hand at keeping case-histories at the much-needed Family Planning Association. 'She loves it! Absolutely loves it! Made a new woman of her. Great success!' he said, as though it were his own success. He had done some good to somebody out here, even if not to himself.

The heat faded into the crisp glowing splendours of October: we had fires in the evenings again. Once or twice small spells of giddiness came upon me, when I neglected to regulate my day in order to take things easily; but the racking pain and sickness were of the past, a horror to be forgotten. Constant worry over someone else can be an effective germicide, apparently, and Barney's pattern of behaviour during this crisis puzzled me more and more. I was too sorry for him to think much about my health.

All this time I had been trying, off and on, to locate Honuong, and not succeeding. She was no longer employed in Cat Street when I went there to look for her again, about a week after my return from Macao.

The old dealer must have been baulked at night once too often. He was short with me when I asked if he had any idea where the girl had gone. None at all. What did it matter? he said. He had secured another young assistant the morning she left.

As amahs do, the mother had drifted away from her job with Mrs. Kenderdine: first, more and more provisions left with her on her day out: then she took to coming back late, and finally had not returned at all. With the tenement and our old house demolished, the family had disappeared into the anonymity of a million other refugees. Because their entry had been unauthorised, nothing about them was registered; there was no tracing them through the police. Even Ah Lee could not help when I appealed to him for help in tracing them, and wash-amah was useless, too. She had come back to us, having lost her baby, but in these days her eyes were often red with crying, she was a joyless creature. This was her third miscarriage, I learnt. Ah Lee was annoyed about it, and had taken up with another concubine, whom he tried to foist on us as second-cook. We gave her one try, at a disastrous dinner party: her sweet reminded me sadly of Third Cousin's, and after that we were adamant against having her in the house. Presumably out of gratitude, wash-amah embroidered another of my handkerchiefs as a Christmas present for me. I was shown it well in advance, and liked it even more than her first effort. Neat black letters in the corner said, 'woe woe life.'

When I had a morning or afternoon free of social duties, which Barney kept on piling up on us, I sometimes took the bus round the coast and wandered about in the most crowded side streets of Kowloon, Wanchai, and Shauky Wan; or if I could get a welfare worker to come with me, on some pretext, walked through one or other of the shanty towns. They were not places to roam about idly, alone. Sooner or later, I thought, I should recognize one of the multitude of passing, scurrying figures as the grandmother, or see the uncle who smoked, leaning up against a wall, and through this encounter be able to locate the others: but it did not happen. The crowding was too great in this fantastic city, and as things

221

were I had too little time to give to the search. I wanted very much to get into Honuong's possession, before I left Hong Kong, a recommendation to whom it might concern that she had every quality necessary for an air hostess. Written by a solid-seeming Hong Kong citizen, it might be the lever which finally lifted her into place where she felt she belonged. Initiative, courage, a strong sense of duty in times of emergency – Remembering the childbirth incident on my roof, I should not even need to lie or so much as stretch the truth for her. If I had been prepared to lie hotly for the sake of Barney, who did not need this consolation, I was ready to do it coolly for the girl who had laid her cheek in my hand, as a daughter should.

Ah Lee, still thinking to put some assistance in his new love's way, suggested that I should give sixpence a week to a young brother of hers, with nothing to do but look about the town for my lost roof-dwellers. I should offer him a shilling if he found them, and we agreed to this arrangement. He came punctually every Monday morning for his sixpence and to report defeat – a glum, shifty-looking lump of a boy, very much like his sister, I thought. But as, every time I passed by Aberdeen anchorage, I saw him messing about on the foreshore there, or talking idly to the junk fishermen, I came to the conclusion that he was brighter than he appeared, though not to my advantage. He realised that with wise inactivity on his part the sixpence-giving might go on idefinitely, while if he ever earned the shilling, that would be the end of gainful employment. He was not going to try. I accepted that for sixpence a week I could hardly expect twelve-hour-a-day service, but as I seemed to be getting none, I kept resolving to tell him, the following Monday, that this was the last payment; and then when Monday came I happened to be busy, Ah Lee saw him and paid him instead; I repaid Ah Lee, and the bargain ran on.

In the hectic weeks before Christmas we invited to our

home people we met at cocktail parties, with whom neither of us was particularly impressed; anything for a fresh face. By this means, cutting across quite a number of the mutually exclusive circles of white society, we may even have done some slight good; a possibility Barney noted with satisfaction. Unfortunately, the sensible Chinese rarely gave or attended cocktail parties: we could not inveigle them in, which would have given me satisfaction.

Barney's war-time shipmate, Commander Lory, was in and out of the flat frequently: something he said in an unguarded moment suggested that he felt Barney had re-covered his old form, despite my pernicious, political in-fluence. Perhaps he was right, I thought. The difference between the way Barney had taken the news of his advance-ment, and the loss of it, remained so perplexing to me that I could find only one explanation. The Barney I was meeting for the first time was no less real than the man under whose roof I lived for years: but this was the Barney of adversity, of Service days in the grimmest part of the war. We had not met then. He had not been like this when our son died, but then he had probably not minded that event as he minded in secret this shattering of his image of himself, as the man adequate to all circumstances. He could not accept defeat: a useful characteristic in war, and like many other war-time virtues, not so good in peace. He had put off being promoted because he was afraid of responsibility, in case he should not succeed. His marriage had not been allowed to fail openly, though we should have been happier apart. And now we were both drawn into this social pretence that all was well: he was on the way to better things.

Ah Lee came into the sitting room one Monday morning, when I was addressing a pile of Christmas cards and thinking it a peculiarly fatuous occupation, this Christmas of all years. He had a way of slipping a piece of local gossip in front of any more personal announcement. 'Resettlement block where old house was, and tenement was, and Weepie Missee was, ready by Christmas!'

'Is it really? They've been wonderfully quick with it,' I said absently.

'You see, there'll be big fire shanty town night before Christmas! You see. Missee, young man is outside for you.'

He always called his temporary brother-in-law 'young man,' to seem as detached as possible from his fortunes. I told him to show the lad in, and as someone walked through the door, kept my eyes on the cards and envelopes in front of me, trying to think out a phrase which would save face for both of us in ending this sixpencey farce.

'You d-don't know me?' said Johnny, and for another second I dared not look up. Then I was across the room and being half stifled by a bear-hug from a hefty young sailor.

'You've grown,' I told him idiotically. 'Oh, Johnny, how you've grown!'

'I come because you was the one per-per – bec-c-c – '

'Don't backtrack,' I said automatically. 'Go on from where you've got to. You've forgotten!'

'No, I haven't – person who could help.'

We sat down soberly, after a minute or two, and, because he wanted it, begged for it, insisted on it, we had a long teaching-session, straight away, interspersed with the saga of his adventures. As I thought, the planning and determination he had shown had been prodigious; there had been false starts, and disappointments galore, long periods at sea when he had more or less given up the idea of getting out to Hong Kong; and the anti-climax of finding that I was somewhere else when he succeeded the first time, he glossed over, not wishing to talk of it. 'When I stopped being a silly kid – ' was his dismissal of the slow death of resentment against me for repeating the pattern of desertion in his young life. I had not the courage to tell him, that morning, I was due to leave Hong Kong in the New Year. There would not be time, between this and then, to do much more than get him back to where he was before. Despite his denial, he had forgotten almost everything under the stresses of his existence in the last eighteen months. The block, when it came, was as painful as ever. But it was wonderful to be teaching him again: wonderful. Here was my son: tiresome and difficult still, probably – I should find that out later – but mine to help.

'You know I've always said, I can't cure your stammer completely? You do remember that, Johnny?' I said anxiously. 'I can only make it so it doesn't spoil your contacts with people.'

'You do that! No-one else can.'

'Well, that's not true. Except that you make it so, for yourself, by thinking I'm the only one who can help.'

'You do that!' he said again. This was what he had come for. There was a girl in San Francisco. He showed me a photograph of her, and of several others. If she didn't wait, well, there were plenty more good fish in the sea – Johnny had indeed grown up.

'Young man' called, and was lucky, getting away with next week's payment without argument, so that we should not be interrupted.

When Johnny left for that day, I sat staring in a happy stupor at the Christmas cards in their envelopes on the table. He would be coming back the next day. And the next, and the next . . . He had worked this last voyage so that he took his discharge from his ship in Hong Kong, where she had been brought to be broken up. Before seeking me out, having enquired in a local shop to make sure I was in residence, he had gone back from Aberdeen to the city and found himself a bed in the Y.M.C.A. which he could afford for a month, and by that time, he said confidently, he would have got himself a job, somewhere around. This was a lad, I thought, whom I should have wanted to help even if he had not been in the least like anyone I had loved.

There were three cards still unwritten, out of fifty or sixty on the list Barney had made of the firm's principal clients, agents, and competitors, and a few personal friends. In effect, I stole them. I addressed one to the almoner at the Clinic. That would surprise her, if she still remembered who I was. (You got no thanks for 'being too soft with people'? Of course not. But sometimes – very rarely, and unbelievably good when it came – the ultimate reward instead: a chance to be fully stretched, to work with everything you had and were.) 'With all good wishes from Chloe Freeborn' I wrote, and meant it.

The second went to Laura Cairns. Barney had said while making the list that he saw no point in our sending her a card to London, when she was just as likely to be spending Christmas in Oslo, or vice versa. At the time I had agreed. But not now. Kind, extraordinary Laura – I owed her friendly cognition on this kind, extraordinary day. And the third was for Tom Jarvis. What harm, after a silence so long? I knew where his ship was. I always knew where his ship was: it was easy in a British colony, in peace-time, to follow the movements of the navy: easier than in England. Treading on air that afternoon, I did something unnecessarily luxurious. Having my hair trimmed, washed and set in the most expensive shop of its kind in Hong Kong was an extravagance which held no lure for me at all in the ordinary way. My hair was my fool-proof feature. I could cut it short with kitchen scissors, and because it was very soft and closely curling it set itself obligingly as if all the chopped off ends were tapered to the same length: I had to be wary, in other women's company, not to sound insufferably smug when the talk turned, inevitably in Peak circles, to the where-do-you-get-yours-so-beautifully-done line of deadly silken competition. But I suddenly wanted the silly smell of a temple of vanity where, I had been warned at many dinner parties, all the prices were slightly higher than in the west-end of London.

The perfume was even heavier and the carpet thicker than I expected when I went into the hairdresser's. The place seemed full of willowy Chinese assistants plucked and painted and eye-shadowed into advertisements of their craft. Over mask-like faces their hair was piled high in elaborate styles, and they looked so opulently unreal it was hard to believe that by the latest Government statistics on the working population, seven out of ten probably emerged from shanty towns each morning, and went back into the filth and squalor there, or to the sort of tenement I knew, when they left these gilded rooms in the evening. They moved about as though on imaginary bound feet.

Behind a desk notice saying 'Miss Cleo,' the head receptionist clicked her regret and her disapproval that Modom had come without an appointment. When the pre-Christmas rush was on, too! No chance, whatever – A smaller replica glided up to her elbow and murmured deferentially that she thought she could work Modom into her schedule if Miss Cleo wished.

'Can you, Gloria?' Miss Cleo sounded dubious, but Gloria, nodding with care so as not to disturb her tall glossy-black helmet, insisted that her next client was always late, she knew exactly how Modom liked her hair styled and was certain she could manage it in the time available.

'Very well, if you're sure. Will Modom follow Gloria, please, to the end cubicle? Isn't Modom fortunate?'

'Yes!' I said. 'I am,' and Gloria's enlarged red lips parted over Honuong's little pointed teeth.

As soon as we were out of sight, in the cubicle, she repeated the charming, ceremonial daughter-salutation, palm to cheek. 'This is my last stop before I go – up there!' she told me, pointing at the ceiling as if indeed she expected to be translated to Heaven. 'Three months I stay here, to get – '

'Polish?' I suggested.

'Ho-ho!' she laughed to my reflection in the well-shaded

mirror. 'Then I try! Ask to see someone in B.O.A.C.'

'And the best of luck, as I've said before. But when you go up for an interview, with whoever it is who takes on hostesses, not too much polish, Honuong! Not, for instance, that hair style.'

'No, no. This is for here. I will look just like your friend – only Chinese. Very quiet and nice. I watch her, remember, the night of the fireworks.'

'You couldn't have a better model. Her appearance, I mean. There's a snag, though, I've only just heard about: through people talking at a party where everyone seemed to fly a lot. They won't take you as an Asian air hostess till you're over twenty-one. How old are you, Honuong? Nothing like that, surely?' I fancied she was younger than Johnny, but she had begun to fill out, now that she was earning better money, and was wholly transformed in face and body from the bony child I had known. She might have been anywhere between sixteen and twenty-six.

'Missee, you have never known. Refugees – who can prove anything? No papers from the places where we are born! All white people say, "Cannot tell the age of a Chinese woman" –' There was the authentic accent of the Peak, *de haut en bas*, in those last few words: I had forgotten what a good mimic she was – and needed to be. 'I tell you, "I am twenty-two." You believe it – or you don't believe it? Never mind. But when I am ready to try, please give me a letter to copy and a chit to say, you think I am the right girl. And put in it "I am told she is twenty-two." Who tells you? I tell you.'

'All right,' I agreed, aware that this was thoroughly reprehensible and not caring at all. Both my children had been returned to me in one day, and I had found the second only because the coming of the first had made me frivolous. 'I'll have to give you that letter and chit now, not when you want it,' I said. 'Could you get me two sheets of paper? The letter-heading of this firm will do nicely – Never mind my hair.'

228

She was snipping at it in the approved way, as she had been taught, back-combing each strand before cutting. 'Just sprinkle some water on it and put it under the dryer, it'll be all right. So we can talk before your other client comes.' Honuong was shocked and would do nothing of the kind: I must go through the proper process, as I should have to pay for it anyway.

'You come in again and give me the papers,' she suggested.

'No, I might not be able to. I'm going back to England, you see. Quite soon.'

'Missee, what a pity.' I did not expect more emotion than that: her own blossoming life was far too enthralling for the loss of a friend to matter now. She fetched me the notepaper, and I dashed off a letter of application and, more carefully written, a personal testimonial, which included the words, 'integrity,' 'initiative,' 'intelligence and ability to inspire confidence.' As I signed this, without having any real evidence that she possessed such qualities, I thought once more what an unsuitable wife I made for Barney: human considerations would always come before principles, for me. I sometimes wondered if I had any principles: lovers of the here and now rarely have.

Looking over my shoulder, Honuong said, 'Should there be, "Of good education"?'

'Well – ' To hesitate over this was perhaps straining at a gnat, but there had to be some limits, for credibility's sake.

'I can read and write Cantonese. And English. Cantonese is difficult. It takes four years to learn! I could do that before I came over the frontier.'

'So you could. "Bring me some muffins".' I inserted 'Of good education' at the end of a line, where it followed on smoothly.

She accepted the two papers without thanks, as though they had been her daily rice. I was touched that despite the enormous change outwardly, inside there was still the child, the firm believer in the established order of things, who, because I had interfered in her emergency, knew that her claim on me was for ever. Her next words took my breath away.

'You go back to England to the man from the big ship that has left? The one who laughs and said, "You cut wood"?'

'What do you know of that man?' After fifteen months in and around Hong Kong, I was still unused to the grape-vine.

'There is a sister-in-law of my mother's sister-in-law, who was not with us on the roof, because she has somewhere to live. A sampan. But she will never let us come into it with her because she says we are land-people. Perhaps she is not quite a sister-in-law –' The involved working out of relationship led, as I might have guessed it would, to the jolly, bawdy woman who had rowed Tom and me across to Kowloon on the night of enchantment.

'Yes, he does laugh quite often.' I said, bemused. 'But I am going back to London with my husband. Where are you living?'

The family was scattered again. Honuong and her grand-mother having the lease of a shelf in a hut in Tai Hang Tung, one of the Kowloon shanty-towns. The old lady slept by day and Honuong, because she was working, by night, except when it rained, and then the whole place was flooded. 'But sometimes I can get an hour here, by day,' she said. 'The lava-tories for customers are very beautiful. You should go to see, if you have time. If Miss Cleo does not notice a girl slip in, she can lock the door and stay there all her lunch time. Every-one thinks it is a customer inside, and does not like to climb up to look over the top of the door. (Because it is not a proper wall all round. Not going the whole way up.) Four times I have had a full hour, when it rained all the night before, and no-one has known.'

She really possessed most of the qualities I had credited her with, I concluded.

The family had applied, along with thousands of others, to

be alloted space in the new resettlement block where our old house had stood. As former residents on this site, they had a better claim than most, but 'We shall not get in,' Honuong said resignedly.

'Why not?'

'Be another little Shek Kip Mei, you wait!' she said, almost echoing Ah Lee's words. 'Just before new block is open. Then, too many people without roofs again. So, no luck for us.'

Though it happened years before Honuong or I came to Hong Kong, the disaster of Shek Kip Mei was known, at least by hearsay, to everyone in the colony. On Christmas night, 1953, the most devastating fire in the history of the island swept through the shanty town there: no-one had ever discovered how many people were burnt to death, but five hundred thousand became homeless in a few hours, and forty-five acres of ground were cleared of their pathetic dwellings. 'Another little Shek Kip Mei' sounded ominous indeed in the mouth of a shanty town squatter. Intentional fires were never meant to spread: a group of neighbours made a spirited bid for priority in housing, and then the wind blew. . . .

'Where will it break out?'

'Near where we are. I told you, Tai Hang Tung.'

'Who will start it?'

Her eyes turned flickery again, as in the old days when I asked about the district where the family had come from – I should never be wholly trusted; I was of the wrong colour.

'How do I know, Missee? Maybe someone upset a kerosene lamp. Not us. No lamp, and we are very careful with our candle.'

Her unpunctual client teetered in on heels even higher than Honuong's and Miss Cleo's, not bothering to explain why she was over twenty minutes late for an appointment. I was hurriedly released from one dryer, put under another in a spare cubicle, and had no further chance of private talk with

Honuong: it was the elegant Eurasian, Miss Cleo, I had to pay.

'Thank you for fitting me in,' I said. 'Gloria has done the job splendidly.'

'She has indeed, Modom, if I may say so. Modom seems quite a different person.' But my head looking exactly as if I had dealt with it myself was hardly a fair test of Honuong's new skill.

In the evening I mentioned to Barney that a rumour had reached me from two Chinese sources of a blaze to come in Tai Hang Tung, before the opening of the new building, some time in Christmas week. He replied characteristically in his war-mood, 'They'll choose a night with a wind, of course, the feckless fools. Let's see, we're dining with the Ogilvies on the 23rd and the Sandersons on the 24th. Both near there. We'll keep an eye lifting if it happens to be blowy weather. Half those big fires could be stopped if two or three men with a bit of sense got on the spot quickly, and didn't wait for the fire engines to arrive. You can put a shoulder to those huts and bring them down, and have a workable fire-break in no time.' (Normally he would have said, 'Well, it's not our affair, is it?')

'Ought we to warn the fire services?' I asked.

'You bet they know. If you've heard of it in advance, so have they: ear-to-the-ground stuff. All that's wanted is a handful of people who don't panic taking charge before the flames really catch hold. Quite a lot of old ladies can be hauled out of burning match-boxes before the officials get on the scene! By the way, I've had an idea for Boxing Day, Chloe. It's always a bit of an anti-climax –'

I had hoped for twenty-four hours of complete rest then, except for a teaching session with Johnny. I was nearly exhausted with pressurised entertaining and being entertained.

' – We've never been to Lau Tau island,' he said. 'Must do that before we leave. There's the famous Buddhist monastery at Ngong Peng.'

'Oh, Barney! It's a four hour climb up a terrific steep hill. Practically a mountain – I've met people who've been. They all say, wonderful when you get there, but grim on the way. Not for me. Not yet.'

'Now or never. As a matter of fact, I thought you might find the climb a bit much. I've engaged a carry-chair to meet us at Silvermine, where we get off the ferry. Two stout coolie women to take you up like baggage. How's that?'

'I'd be ashamed to be carried up a mountain by two other, sweating women. For pleasure.'

'Nonsense. They'll be glad of the money. There's a bonze at Ngong Peng who's set himself the task of banging a huge gong every thirty seconds for six years. He's been at it a year and a half now. I want to see what shape he's in. We get back just after dark, and then – supposing you aren't too tired, we could phone to put them off if necessary – the Kenderdines are coming in for coffee. It's uncanny what family-planning has done for her. You'll be amazed.'

CHAPTER XV

Shanty Town Fire

THE BLAZE STARTED on the night of the Ogilvie's dinner-party. We arrived late at their house, and saw the flicker under a trail of smoke high up on the hillside about half a mile away.

Our lateness was my fault and Barney, the soul of punctuality, had been irritable about it all the way round the coast in a taxi from Aberdeen. If I had been ready on time we could have caught the local bus to the Star Ferry, and it was a long, expensive ride: the Ogilvies lived over the water in Kowloon. Neither then nor at any time afterwards had I the nerve to point out that if I had not made us late, he would not have noticed the fire in its early stages soon enough to take effective action.

What had delayed me was that Johnny had turned up half-way through the afternoon, jubilant at having secured himself a temporary job in one of the ship-building yards which might lead on to something permanent. He wanted a lesson at once: this was his idea of a celebration. We settled down to a series of breathing and easing-out exercises. Teaching Johnny when he was bent on learning was so delightfully different from teaching Johnny when he was putting up a savage resistance, as in days gone by, that I lost all sense of time. We found ourselves laughing together over that first interview of ours. 'Remember how brutally I had to force you to acknowledge that the boys at school made fun of you?'

'And now it's g-girls that get under my s-skin!' he said. 'Which is worse!' But obviously it was not.

'You do remember, I can't cure you completely?' I repeated. 'Only make you able to cope, pretty comfortably, with what's left of an impediment?'

'You do that,' he said again. 'Just do that! Oh, Lord, I've come a long way – ' and then he was off on his experiences again, and because he was now a shipyard employee I explained 'Leisured Persons Avoid Advance': we did another set of exercises to deal with his fear of certain words, and suddenly it was seven o'clock and I should have started dressing at six thirty.

On the ferry, as we crossed to the Kowloon side, Barney said that he was glad I was getting my hand in again for work; he was particularly glad that this patient, in whom I took an interest, had turned up again: it was just that being late was unnecessarily discourteous to the Ogilvies – The feeling of unreality which had enveloped him, so far as I was concerned, ever since I came back from Macao, increased to the point where I felt that I was living beside him in a dream. This man, bothering so much about trifles, in a mental lapse from a state of euphoria – what relation, if any, was he to the man who had written the crushed and miserable letter which had brought me back to Hong Kong in a hurry, the dreadful letter in which he had briefly faced and acknowledged that he was a failure?

In the interval between our ring at the Ogilvie's front door and its opening by Ogilvie himself, the flames had reached out on a stiff breeze to envelop four or five more tinder-huts. They blazed like torches in the night. All thought of what was due to our hosts and their dinner party was immediately laid aside by Barney: he took charge, and organized himself, Ogilvie, and the other male guest into the quorum of 'men who could be relied on not to panic,' required to prevent another Shek Kip Mei. Prevent it they did, valiantly; though at one moment, a little before the official fire-fighting equipment arrived, it looked touch and go to me. I thought that the flames and the wind together were winning against their efforts.

A blaze in a shanty town has a peculiar, nightmare quality of horror, comparable with the effects of bombing in slum areas during the war. Close-packed, humanity becomes more helpless, flesh seems more vulnerable. A flimsy partition falls, burning, and there are all the household goods of a family displayed, luridly lit as though they had some tremendous significance, and in a few seconds more, they are obliterated, utterly consumed.

Standing upwind of the fire with Mrs. Ogilvie, and the wife of the man whose name I never knew, I tried, as they did, to help in passing back to safety the belongings of those whose huts were in the path of the fire. But no-one would trust any-one else with his or her handful of goods. Afterwards, I remembered from that evening, more clearly than anything else, a cooking-pot steaming on a charcoal brazier, in a shelter burning too fiercely to allow anything more to be salvaged. The brazier was on a makeshift packing-case table, and this, too, had begun to burn. By a pointless miracle the brazier subsided through the table with the pot still balanced on it, and whatever was inside went on cooking, while the shelter collapsed about it. Till it was hidden by a fall of burning debris, it looked touchingly peaceful and domestic.

Making effective fire-breaks was not easy for the three men: the families directly menaced by the fire were too busy looking after their own possessions, and their relatives', to give any systematic help. They beat at the flames with improvised flails, till the flames menaced their property, and then concentrated on moving as much of this as they could. Those whose huts were outside the danger zone were not going to be embroiled in other people's catastrophes. They stood round in a vast idle crowd.

The shanties had proliferated, wherever the steep slope of the ground allowed, not in rows but one out of another on all sides, cactus-like. A huddle of several shelters would flare up together, and the flames roared round in a half circle to attack in an unexpected direction. I saw the wind, helped by the updraught from the heat, toss high in the air a flaring piece of tarred cotton, a favoured roofing material, and it landed on the further side of a gap where a rickety structure had just been pulled down. The roof on which it settled must have been of similar stuff: it caught before anyone could beat out the rag.

Grimed, and soon considerably torn and singed, Barney and his mates crashed into huts and threw out whimpering chow puppies and tethered hens, before using their concerted strength against the supports. An old man with paralysed legs, who had just been rescued, kept urging them to go back into what had become a tunnel of flame. For a moment, from his agitation, it seemed likely that there was another living thing in his hut, but it was his palliasse and bed-rags he wanted, probably all he owned in the world, and when he knew he had lost them he sat near my feet, his face working with distress.

Though I looked about for them, I caught no glimpse of Honuong and her family in the crowd of onlookers.

The Ogilvies were newly married: Mrs. Ogilvie was frightened for her husband, heroically plunging about where smouldering roof-ties fell near him. She apologised to me for showing her agitation when a shanty being torn down collapsed towards him, knocking him over, and for a moment she thought he was pinned down ahead of the advancing fire.

'Of course I know it's just as bad for you!' she said, when he had scrambled up out of the wreckage.

Far from it: incidentally, I could see that Barney – white teeth grinning in a dirtied face as he ran past us – was having a most exhilarating evening. He was in his element, and out of everyday kindness – not love or anxiety – I was pleased that he could be happy in the circumstances.

The fire had been delayed, and more or less contained, when the professionals arrived. The amateur fire-fighters gave up, and we went back to the slightly spoilt dinner, which ushered in quite a jolly social evening all the same. The mood of exhilaration held for Barney. He had a nasty looking burn on one arm from a flaming edge of plank which had slid down from a roof while he and Ogilvie were shoving a hut over; but he refused to delay the party any longer by getting it properly dressed at the nearest hospital, or doctor's, and made do with my ministrations. The gathering broke up about three o'clock in the morning, and then we slept on chairs in the Ogilvie's dining room, going home the next morning in borrowed day-clothes: Barney had conducted his happy campaign in an evening shirt, complete with black tie, and dress trousers, which were ruined.

By the time we reached Aberdeen, Honuong's family, with three new relatives I had not met before, were well settled in on our roof. There was no effort at concealment this time.

Honuong was away at work, but the old lady leant over the parapet waving to us as we approached, for Barney, too, had now embroiled himself in the family misfortunes and could be relied on to accept his responsibility: from then on she and the others maintained firmly that one of the shelters he had pushed down to make a fire-break had been theirs. Ah Lee had been given twenty-four hours' leave to go and stay with his new concubine, or they would never have reached the roof.

'Oh, well, we'll be here such a short time now,' Barney said, still with his cheerful war-spirit about him, 'we might as well let them stay! They're fearful opportunists. But whoever comes here after us will have to cope with that.'

They not only stayed: all the remains of our Christmas lunch went up to them openly the following day, to the returned Ah Lee's silent disgust: and Barney agreed that I should add a blanket apiece, as a present from both of us, to replace their hard-won store of sacking bed-clothes which he had allowed to burn. Officially, at any rate.

Their flowered china container for drinking water and all their cooking pots had inexplicably survived the fire. So had the original shelter, which they had rigged up again. No face-losing reference to this strange selectivity of destruction was ever made, by hosts or guests: they were all destitute again, they insisted, through the disaster, which had as usual made homeless far more people than the new resettlement block, or several such, could possibly house.

I found in a nearby secondhand store, full of Victorian treasures, a commode of really splendid proportions, and elaborate carving. For goodwill, because it was our religious festival, and no other customer was likely to come along during the holiday, the dealer allowed me to take it away for five Hong Kong dollars (six shillings and threepence). In-stalled under the shelter it was enormously admired, and I could only prevent it from being used as a rice-store by pretending that I should inspect it every day, to make sure it was put to its proper purpose. Thereafter there was comparative peace on our roof, except between the family and Ah Lee.

He knew that he would not be able to extort delayed rent, as with his own relatives, when Honuong's people drifted away to jobs, if they ever did. When he gardened for us, in his spare moments, he was apt to complain that the old lady crept down at night to empty the commode over his most recent work, it being known to all that women's excrement is not only useless to flowers, but damaging. He went on gardening enthusiastically, however, in spite of his awareness that this Master's time in office was nearly over. I suspected that as in the last place, he had decided to go with the house. In that case, the squatters would be ejected the moment after we left.

On Christmas Day, seeing that Barney's arm was still painful, I said, 'You surely don't still want to go to Lau Tau island tomorrow?'

'Of course I do. Anyway, we've got the carry-chair booked.'

'Yes, but that's for me. You can't go scrambling up a steep hillside for hours with an arm out of action.'

'I can. Don't fuss. I've had the burn looked at by a doctor. It's all right.'

'Oh, have you? I didn't know.'

'Besides, I've written to the Abbot to ask if we can come. That's purely a formality. He never says no. And we shan't be seeing him personally. All the same, as I have written for permission –'

'But he'd understand if you wrote and said you'd had an accident.'

'We're not leaving Hong Kong without seeing Ngong Peng monastery, and that bonze.'

'All right. Barney, have you heard yet? Exactly when we go?' I had tried hard not to ask that question, not to nag, but

Johnny – Honuong – once more it seemed to me I had much to lose, where I was.

'No, I haven't. But I'll hear any time now.'

So early in the morning we set off. It was a glorious looking day. The ferry was comfortably empty, with only one transistor radio playing on our part of the deck. On the island the track wound upwards over bare, golden slopes, and then through leafy tunnels of dense shadow, and out again on to the hillside where the dried up grass was singing – there was a great wind.

The two strong coolie women who had met us at the ferry carried me up, up, up, resting very occasionally and never for more than a minute or so at a time, except when a young, sad-eyed Buddhist nun with a shaven head came out of a high-walled convent and sold us glasses of exceptionally weak tea. Unburdened, Barney had trouble at times, where the going was roughest, in keeping up with the pace at which I was hoisted along, the chair tilting this way and that when the women scrambled, bent nearly double, up the steepest places.

I was somewhat ashamed of being carried, but it was also shockingly enjoyable. Perched high up on the chair, with my feet dangling between the poles resting on their shoulders, I had an uninterrupted view of the scenery. At every bend in the track, when we were in the open, I could look behind me to where the sea glimmered below us like shot silk: the sunlight silvered it and the cloud shadows turned it all the hues between deep blue and lilac and grey.

The only drawbacks to my position – I had not expected to be six or seven feet above the ground – was that I could discover no way of telling when the two women, in one concerted movement, would shift the position of the poles on their shoulders by a violent shrug. A sign meaning 'Now!' must have passed between them, but watch as I would, I never saw it. Tossed like a pancake, I nearly lost the chair each time, and clung to the arms when I felt that the unpadded poles had been pressing on the same spot for a long time. There was a little swing contraption, a piece of stick in a loop of cord, for me to rest my feet on, but at the unfortellable moment of the jerk and heave it had always slipped from under them. My other source of discomfort was the women's sure-footed habit, reputed to be shared by mules, of walking along the extreme outer edge of the track when there was a long, sheer, boulder-ended drop on that side. Never having ridden a mule, I was not sure whether these creatures really suffered from such an odd compulsion; but the carriers certainly did. Most of the time I managed to avert my eyes.

Talking very fast, despite their exertions, they discussed me in intimate detail, assuming that if I knew any Cantonese, which was unlikely, it would not be of a ripe-flavoured kind. But this was what I had picked up on the roof. I missed some of the phrases over which they both giggled, but got enough to know that I should have had little success with my looks as a Chinese. Too tall in the nose, too mean in the mouth, rump at the front instead of the back (not enough buttock and too much breast) – I earned all the criticisms usually given to European women. My conscious pleasure in the singing golden grass, and in coming through serious ear-trouble without deafness resulting, made me suddenly and unnaturally bold: I decided to answer back, if I could. Carefully I put together and offered, 'This fit-for-squat-on thing considered – by some – not all so fit-for-squat-on in England,' and after a horrified pause they joined me in delighted laughter because I had understood. (I know someone who would have laughed, too. It was not actually very funny. Not in the least witty. But love could have made it seem so.) Now Clo – Old Clo. Stop that. The singing grass is enough.

The carriers very nearly tipped me out of the chair on that occasion, staggering about the path and constantly exploding into fresh mirth. On ahead for once, Barney turned back to ask what the noise was about. The women, still laughing, insisted I must not tell him: after all, he was the one who was going to pay them. 'Later!' I said, aware – with all the silly fun going out of the situation – that he would find what I had done undignified, as he subsequently did. He was right, of course. It was. 'I had no idea you had such a command of Cantonese smut. Or any Cantonese, come to that.'

For the rest of the way up I had a difficult time socially, because the carriers assumed that I knew far more Cantonese than I did, and poured out cheerful complaints against their good-for-nothing sons, along with questions about my family: were my sons, too, lacking in respect for parents, unlike ourselves – Ho-ho, indeed – we were different at the same age? This, at least, was what I fancied I was being re-quired to say. Thinking of Johnny and Honuong again I maintained that my children were not, in fact, worthless, but gave much cause for worry; and we agreed, or I thought we did, that this was how all children were, in these bad days, which were rapidly becoming worse, ho-ho, were they not?

When we reached the monastery, near the top of the peak, and the women put me down at the lovely round moongate, there stood a pair of young Chinese oafs, in tight, European clothes, waiting for their sweating mothers to hand over the chair-money. The women gave it all at once, not only the sum – two pounds – arranged at the time of the engagement, but also the tip Barney had added. A look – 'We are women, what else can we do?' passed between them and me as we said quite an affectionate goodbye. There was a longer but gentler road back, round the mountain, downhill for seven miles. Barney, whose arm was hurting him considerably I could see from the way he carried it, decided that I could easily walk this.

A group of fellow pilgrims were leaving as we arrived. All young male Chinese, they had presumably spent the night in the monastery, as the island's first boat of the day was the one by which we had come, and they looked like smart, city products, not local people. They carried as luggage a tiny transistor, from which a powerful female voice with an American accent, real or assumed, was wailing, 'Could it be you?' before they were two hundred yards away down the path. In another ten years, if Japan keeps up her export drive, the Far East will be intolerable for anyone with an allergy for incongruous music.

In the visitors' refectory, the remnants of their morning meal had not yet been cleared away when we were ushered in by the listless bonze who was acting as brother-hospitaller. All the bowls had been left ominously full. Eyeing the remains, our host assured us that our refreshment would be brought very soon, and it arrived after a pause only long enough to warm up partially, some unidentifiable lumps floating in thin, bitter liquid. In a land where practically everyone, rich or poor, cooked vegetables deliciously, it was surprising to be given a strictly vegetarian meal which proved uneatable, at any rate by us. The depressed, brown-robed bonze looked as if he feared it would be, when he brought it. He volunteered that in the monastery's own refectory the others were at the moment eating their morning meal, and of exactly the same food. We could go and look at the room if we liked, when they had finished.

Our meal was provided free, but it was naturally understood that the visitor would make an offering of something more than its value to the monastery funds. We decided in muttered consultation that the Hong Kong equivalent of half a crown each should cover this. Sighing, the bonze took the four dollars and drifted away, to join his brothers at their meal. Unsafe as it was to generalise on one experience, I concluded that food and drink were less well regarded in Buddhistic religious circles than in the monastic life of the West: at Ngong Peng the lowness of the diet may have accounted for the fact that all but one of the monks we saw afterwards, wandering about their business in the courtyards or in the small surrounding temples, appeared strikingly unChinese in their lack of energy and interest in what they were doing – placing censors on tables before altars, and bowing, and removing them again. Along the sky-line, charming dragons writhed as they always did on temple roofs, but the human guardians of the Good Spirit rarely looked up from the ground. Several of these dedicated men seemed touchingly young, about fifteen, and one or two were even adolescently spotty, which was something I had never seen before, out East, Chinese skin being exceptionally fine-textured and generally flawless, in men and women alike. Inanition may also have explained the tear-off calendar on the bonzes' refectory wall, among the more customary, stylised pictures of sages with their disciples. An enterprising Hong Kong provision merchant, whose name it bore, must have sent it to the Abbot as an advertisement: on it, in a coloured photograph, a juicy-looking Chinese girl knelt with her cheongsam slit half-way up the thigh, and a coy, come-and-get-it expression on her smiling face. The claims of the flesh could have very little chance against those weary, acid vegetables, and practically no protein.

The one exception to the listlessness of the bonzes we met was the man we had come specially to see. His great gong, clanging out at intervals, led us to the little tower where he sat. I had been expecting a particularly grave ascetic but he was a merry little gnarled man, who stayed his hand when he heard us coming till I was standing, inadvertently in the gloom, close beside the gong. The contrast with the brilliant sunshine outside was blinding for the moment. Then he crashed the two-handled clapper against the metal, and was highly amused at having made me jump.

Very much, in his presence, I regretted that my Cantonese was restricted to the simple, low, and practical. There was no interpreter handy: Barney had for some reason assumed that there would be. Both of us would have liked to talk to this man, to find out, if we could, without being impertinent in our questions, what lay behind his curious undertaking. But I had no words for 'acquiring merit,' nor for any other spiritual conception.

I knew that in his faith, 'penance' and 'guilt,' as understood by the West, had no part: I was probably, myself, instinctively nearer to being a Buddhist than a Christian because I had never been able to feel, like Barney, that right and wrong existed, that any one course of action was intrinsically good and another intrinsically bad, irrespective of the human beings who took the actions; but the bonze and I could only meet with our eyes, when my sight returned in the gloom, and wish one another well. I was charmed to discover that he had so far come to terms with his exacting soul that he could allow himself a little modest cheating. When he wanted to accompany us to the monastery gate, as he did with great courtesy – and, no doubt, when he needed to eat, sleep or do anything else – he piled up temporary credit by swinging the clapper in short, rapid strokes, bang-bang-bang-bang-bang, till he had enough time in hand for his purpose.

Barney and I started gaily down the mountain side. It was still early afternoon and our ferry would not leave till nearly six o'clock, but if I were to be able to rest occasionally on the way we needed a good two hours. Though exceedingly hungry, we had both enjoyed our day, in the sense of finding it extremely interesting, and we were unusually friendly together. Mile after mile, in this clear, wonderful air, we could see the track winding down before us, round the contours of the hill, disappearing into folds and reappearing again, on and on.

'Don't overdo it, Chloe,' Barney said quite solicitously, as I strode ahead at one point, afraid if I slackened my pace I'd never get across this vast expanse of country, down to the sea. 'I suggest you have a breather, here and now.'

'All right.' We sat down, just off the path, our backs against boulders, and I noticed again the high, thin singing of the grass in the dry wind.

Barney said, 'As a matter of fact, I wanted a rest! You were quite right, this was an idiotic expedition to take with a burnt arm! Every time I've moved it suddenly, without thinking, and my shirt pulled over the bandage – Oh Lord! I did it again just now. All the same, I've enjoyed the whole thing.'

It was so rare for Barney to admit himself in the wrong I warmed to him and said, not meaning this seriously, 'I'm afraid I've let you down twice today with my Cantonese, once by knowing too much, and then not enough.' It was true that I was forever letting him down, one way and another. I had a perpetually apologetic feeling towards Barney, he was so much the better person of the two of us. But for once, at the moment I was not conscious of being in the wrong: I said in a cheerful, argumentative tone: 'Still, if you hadn't realized before that I knew any at all you couldn't have expected – ' My voice tailed off. He was not listening. With an intent face he was looking at a root of grass he had just pulled out of the ground as though he had never seen such a plant before.

'You don't really want to come back to England with me, do you?' he asked, the words jerked out of him suddenly.

The turning earth stopped for me, and then rolled on. This could mean anything, or nothing: freedom, for me, or no more than a sudden feeling of inadequacy on his part.

Listening very carefully to my own voice, to keep it even – as I had been forced to do on another occasion – I asked, dry-mouthed, 'Would you rather I didn't?' If the choice were his, in our parting, there would be no sense of defeat in it, for him.

He considered this for a moment, and my heart hammered so that it became hard to breath. First, barring me from a life of my own, there had been the need to protect Clive. And then, when that was over, came the foreknowledge that

Barney would lose this job, and I could not, must not hurt him further. How odd that women were always supposed to long to be needed, and all I wanted at the moment was to be assured that I was not.

'You must please yourself,' he insisted. 'But you know, Chloe, I sometimes feel we bring out the worst in one another, you and I.'

I gasped, and was aware of a terrible temptation to laugh; hysterically, I knew. I almost prayed: Don't let me laugh – for his sake – for my sake. After the first shock and disappointment of his dismissal, he had not seemed to care. Most strangely, he, in whom pride was so vulnerable, had taken this humiliation almost with indifference.

'It's Laura Cairns, isn't it?' I asked, not knowing till the words came that I was going to use them.

'Yes,' he said, after a long pause.

'You want to marry her, when you're free?' (We can't be saying these things, I thought. Not Barney and I. But we were.)

'Yes, I do. You see, Chloe, I believe I can help her. Really be of some use to her.'

'Oh, I'm sure you can,' I said, feeling as if I were giving a testimonial to someone I hardly knew. 'I expect you're just the sort of person she needs. To steady her. When – ?'

'When what?'

'When did this start? With Laura?'

'Why should you want to know that?'

'I can't say, really. It doesn't matter, does it, when it started? But I'd like to know.'

'Well – this isn't particularly nice, and I'm afraid it may hurt you – '

Hurt? With the glory of the day crying in the wind? 'No, it won't.'

'It was while you were ill, I'm sorry to say. Right at the beginning. When Laura – '

' – was going on long leave! And put it off for a few days to look after things for you. She's very kind, as we've always said. Oh, Barney – ' Laura on long leave. Laura saying, 'You know I never do . . . except on long leave.' And then the desire to laugh, partly from happiness, became almost irresistible. 'I do think you're right,' I told him. 'Somehow we do seem to bring out the worst in one another. I'm sorry about that. My fault, no doubt.' I should not have to go on apologising for almost everything, being forever in the wrong! 'Look, you won't actually have to support me – never mind what's arranged in Court. You've got so many commitments, and here comes another. Though I'm sure Laura will want to go on working – Oh, Barney, we can't be saying all this. Ten minutes ago I was bound back to a life we both know I'm not suited for, and now we're talking about what I'll live on, out here, when you go!'

But we went on talking about it, wandering down the enormous hill; and at one time, in a moment of mutual gratitude, holding hands. It was a little sad – but only a little – only in the way all change is a little sad – that two people who had lived in the same house for years could part with such indifference.

'You see, Laura's never really had a chance,' Barney was saying earnestly, when we sat down to rest for the second time. 'Not of a reasonable home life. I want to give her security.' And I reminded him, for his comfort, that I had been quite a competent secretary, before I became a speech therapist. I could be a secretary again. 'Take a refresher course. Industry's crying out for women in all sorts of jobs. Out here, in this expanding economy – Honestly, Barney, dear, you don't have to worry about me.'

Of course I should have foreseen this coming-together of Barney and Laura: it was only on the surface that it seemed highly improbable. For Barney, the attraction of the lame duck – the morally frail duck in this instance – and the self-thwarting instinct, focussing on one object, made Laura irresistible. Deep down, he must have known that Laura was not ripe for reclamation, being fundamentally innocent, frigid and kind. I wished them both all the luck in the world, but doubted that they would have it together.

These were second thoughts, which came when we were walking on again, rounding the lower foothills, almost down to sea level. Inwardly, I amended my 'I expect you're just what she needs,' to 'I accept that she is what you need.' Aloud, I said, 'I would like you to be happy. Tell her when you see her that I said that, and meant it.'

A fish-eagle sailed over on superb, motionless wings, a beautiful thing of power and freedom. Its shadow swept close by us on the singing grass, and my heart soared with the bird, no freer than I was.

I could hardly put one foot in front of the other to get on to the ferry: my body was completely exhausted. The ten or twelve mile walk had been far too much for me, still weak from the lingering effects of months of illness. But the lights of Hong Kong and the Kowloon shore, which were springing out everywhere as the ferry brought us in at dusk, were more splendid and exhilarating than they had ever looked to me before. I said, 'Let's take the Peak tramway and have dinner in the hotel at the top, instead of going home. The city's so gorgeous from up there, in the dark.'

We did, and had a bottle of wine with the meal, on the excuse that we had fed so poorly that day: neither of us would face openly that this was a celebration.

CHAPTER XVI

Bread upon Waters

FOR SIX MONTHS after Barney went back to England I stayed on in Hong Kong, living in the little house on Aberdeen Bay, with a varying assortment of Honuong's relatives living above. Aberdeen was really too far from any available centre of work to be convenient for them: one, having secured a job elsewhere, was always disappearing, to be replaced, sooner or later. The supply appeared to be endless. The grandmother was the only unchanging element.

Ah Lee stayed with me as well, and their feud continued spasmodically. I made do financially managing the European correspondence of several small export businesses and, after a time, when I had taken the course I had promised myself, acting as rush-time secretary, filling in staff shortages for a number of bigger firms. This was quite interesting: it brought me in contact with new, small worlds. There was a detached, interim feeling about this period, while far away in England the dreary business of the divorce went through.

It felt very peculiar to me, being the aggrieved party. I woke one morning, about a fortnight after Barney had been replaced and flown away, with a strong sense of relief. I had at last realized with my heart and not only my mind that what I had told myself on Lau Tau island was true, and important to me. I had no more need to be constantly in the wrong about anything. I must have resented feeling inferior so often, even more than I knew. The here and now glowed again.

At first, out of remorse on both sides I suppose, Barney and I wrote to one another, almost as often as we had done when I was convalescing in Japan and Macao. Our final leave-taking had been hurried and practical: at the last hour his ticket had been switched to an earlier flight, because of the grounding in Tokyo of the plane by which he should have travelled. 'Remember Ah Lee's pay-book is in the left-hand drawer, and it's paid up to the fifteenth of next month.' – 'Yes. yes. Give Laura my love. I mean that. Please tell her I mean that.'

Gradually, as the weeks went by, the letters tailed off. What a queer marriage ours had been. Perhaps all marriages were equally strange, but one could only know about one's own.

I saw Honuong into the air, the sprucest looking little vixen imaginable. In her regulation and very becoming cheongsam she bore hardly any resemblance either to the bony child of fifteen months ago, or the recent, elaborate concoction of Miss Cleo's salons: she was gloriously sedate. I loosed her to her new world almost with as much sense of achievement as she herself felt. Even seen from backview she shone with the triumph of that moment as she walked up the steps to stand in the plane beside the regular Asian hostess, waiting for her first training flight to begin.

And I saw Johnny through his own battle, to the point where his stammer was no more than a characteristic way of catching, for a second or two, on certain words: always unexpected words. He would never be able to tell just when the block would come. But it was so slight, it was rather endearing. He really was, as I told him, the vindication of the van Riper method. I had never known it work better. He began planning – he had kept his sea papers – to make his way back as a deck hand to San Francisco, where with any luck that girl whose photograph he kept was still around. Or if not, there would be others. A lot of smasheroos, he said, the girls of San Francisco. Once they had laughed at him. Let girls beware.

All this time I remained undecided whether to throw in my lot permanently with Hong Kong, putting myself so hard to the study of Cantonese that perhaps, eventually – two or three years hence, with some further specialised training – I might be able to follow my own profession in another language. Those admirably balanced people, the Chinese, had far fewer speech defects than were common in our tenser western civilisations, but – ho-ho – there were some. Or by economising strictly till I had saved the fare and something over, should I return to England, to struggle back on my own ground? But one factor in the argument which went to and fro in my own mind, the background to all other thoughts, was something that I could not decide, and it outweighed all the rest. It is not possible for a woman to approach a man she loves and say, in effect, I have no way of telling what your feelings are towards me. Whether anything remains. I know my own, that's all, and I am free.

Ah Lee said, 'Cable for Missee from Beirut,' one day when I came in wearily from work. 'Post Office say, too late to send messenger all this way. You phone them, or you wait till morning.'

'Beirut? I don't know anyone in Beirut.' And then it occurred to me that it might be Johnny in some kind of trouble. I reached for the telephone.

Tom Jarvis had cabled 'Have weeks leave shall I come Hong Kong we might dance,' and then I knew it was all right. What one person means to another should not be reckoned in money, but I looked up the air fare from Beirut to Hong Kong at once, and it was £320. No man, neither mad nor a millionaire, spends so much in order to dance in Hong Kong, lovely as the city is, lying among her Nine Dragon Hills.

Some time later, when everything was settled for me, I asked him how he knew, in Beirut, where he was working on another airfield extension, that my marriage had broken up in a small Chinese fishing town, about a quarter of the way round the world.

Tom said, 'I met a Chinese air hostess in Jakarta. We got talking about where she came from. I asked if she knew you, in Hong Kong. She told me you lived alone, in these days.

252

But at the time I couldn't do anything. I'd got no leave due to me. I had to go back to Beirut and wait.'

'Did you get her name?'

'No.'

'Had she a face like a nice little fox? Needle-sharp teeth?'

'Come to think of it, yes she had.'

'You get no thanks . . .'? A voice echoed out of the past. No, indeed, why should anyone expect reward for the self indulgence of being 'too soft with people'? This is a luxury. But, very occasionally, instead of thanks come all the glories earth can offer. There is no moral about this. It is far more likely not to happen. But it happened to me.